Zeb Pike

Boy Traveler

Illustrated by James Ponter

Zeb Pike

Boy Traveler

By Augusta Stevenson

THE **BOBBS-MERRILL** COMPANY, INC.
A SUBSIDIARY OF HOWARD W. SAMS & CO., INC.
Publishers • INDIANAPOLIS • NEW YORK

Illustrations

Full Pages

Numerous smaller illustrations

Contents

Books by Augusta Stevenson

Zeb Pike

Boy Traveler

Out on Bald Eagle Creek

"WHY CAN'T I sleep in the loft?" asked young Zebulon Pike. "You put my bed up there."

"This is our first night in this cabin," said his mother. "You're not used to sleeping alone."

"I'm not afraid."

"Oh, of course not! But you've been sleeping in the wagon with your father and me ever since we left Bucks County. Why don't you get into the trundle bed with your brother? You've always slept with him."

"You said I didn't have to sleep in a trundle bed after we came out here, Mother."

"I know, but you could sleep in it tonight."

"Trundle beds are for babies," said the boy. "I'm over eight years old."

"You're three months over," said his father. "You had a birthday on January fifth, this year, 1787."

"That was when we lived in Pennsylvania."

"We still live in Pennsylvania, Zeb. We just moved west to this place on Bald Eagle Creek."

Zeb was not interested in his father's words. There was something else on his mind. "You said I could put my things in the loft, Mother. I carried my rocks and bird nests up there this afternoon."

"That's all right, Zeb. It's your room. I was afraid you would hear strange noises in the night. There are wild animals on the ridge just across the creek, and we are close to the bank."

"Noises won't scare me."

"Zeb wants to be a frontier boy," said his father. "Maybe he should sleep alone."

"Well, maybe he should," said Isabella Pike. "Call us if you get scared, Zeb."

The boy was halfway up the ladder when he stopped. "It's dark up there. I need a candle."

"Frontier boys don't use candles to undress by, son," said Captain Pike. "They're not afraid of the dark."

"I'm not afraid either," said Zeb. Then he went on up into the loft.

His parents heard his shoes drop on the floor. Then there was silence.

Captain Pike spoke softly. "That boy is head-strong, Isabella. I'm afraid we'll have trouble with him out here. He'll want to do the same things he did on our farm back in Bucks County."

"I'm afraid so. He's been used to close neighbors and real roads. He was free to come and go. He can't do that here."

"Indeed he can't!" exclaimed the Captain.

Zeb heard his parents' voices for a time. When he couldn't hear them, he knew they were asleep. It didn't seem right. It was just as if they had gone away and left him.

Now the night noises began. Owls hooted near by. Far away were sounds Zeb had never heard before—howling and strange cries.

Suddenly there was a loud scream just outside—a terrible scream. It sounded like a woman. The boy was so frightened he wanted to go downstairs, but he didn't even get up.

"Mother! Father!" he called. "I'm scared!"

"I'm coming, Zeb!" Almost at once his father was in bed with him holding him close.

"It was a panther you heard, son. But it was across the creek on the ridge. The wind blew the sound this way and made it seem close by."

The next thing Zeb knew Mother was calling him to breakfast. He tried to talk about the panther at the table. But his parents made light of it.

14

"You'll hear them screaming on the ridge," said his father. "They won't come over here. They stay away from clearings and people."

"Will bears or wolves come over?"

"No. We're perfectly safe. All the clearings are on this side of the creek. The ridge is too steep and too rocky for farms, so we'll let the animals have it for themselves."

Now Mrs. Pike asked Zeb to take Jimmie outside. "He needs this nice sunshine," she said. "He's not feeling very well this morning."

This worried Zeb. He loved his three-year-old brother dearly. "Is he sick again, Mother?"

"No, but you know he's never very well. Don't let him play. Just walk in our clearing, and take the dog along."

In a half hour Zeb brought his brother back. "We walked along the creek bank," he said. "I showed him the ridge on the other side, and you should have heard him laugh at King."

15

"What did King do?" asked Captain Pike.

"He saw a rabbit across the creek and wanted to chase it. I could hardly hold him back."

"You must never allow him to cross over, and you must never cross yourself."

"Couldn't I go after him if he does?"

"No indeed!"

"I could wade across quickly and come right back with him."

"I forbid you to cross that creek," said the Captain. "Do you understand?"

"Yes, sir."

That night, Zebulon Pike, frontier boy, slept in the trundle bed with his brother. No one had told him to, either.

WAS IT A DREAM?

Zeb was outside with Jimmie the next morning when their nearest neighbor came. He was

Mr. Edward White—his farm was a mile or so down the creek from the Pike's farm.

"Don't let the children come in," he said. "They shouldn't hear what I have to say. I found bear tracks in my barnyard this morning."

"I was told they wouldn't come over here."

"They will if they are hungry, Captain."

"Would panthers come, too?" asked Mrs. Pike.

"Any wild beast will go anywhere for food. All we can do is to get rid of them, and I think we should begin at once."

"I'll join a hunt any time, sir."

"I'll get the settlers together. I'll let you know. Oh, Mrs. Pike, my wife wants you to come to see her. She's down with ague."

"I'll come tomorrow," said Isabella. "Perhaps I can help her. I'm a good doctor."

"She doctored all the people in the neighborhood back home," said Captain Pike. "She cured most of them, too."

"My wife will be mighty glad to see you, Ma'am," said Mr. White. "Now good day to both of you."

"Well!" exclaimed Mrs. Pike when they were alone. "Bears, panthers, wolves, and wildcats! I'm glad I know how to shoot."

"After we kill a few, the others will leave. In the meantime I'll carry a gun everywhere."

"I'll keep mine loaded and close at hand."

Supper was just over when Mr. White came back. "My wife is worse," he said gravely. "She's shaking so hard she's shaking the bed. I've done everything I can. Have you any medicine?"

"I haven't any made up, but I have the herbs. The tea will stop her chills if it's made right. I'll go back with you and make it myself. I'll be ready in a minute."

"I'll hitch my team to the cart," said Captain Pike. "We'll drive over, Mr. White." He left the cabin and took his gun with him.

18

"Can you leave your children, Ma'am?" asked Mr. White.

"They'll be safe with the door barred. Don't go outside, Zeb, and keep Jimmie in. Bar the door and close the window shutters as soon as we go. I'll leave the beef on the table. You might get hungry before we come back."

Then they left. Zeb pulled the latchstring in and put the heavy bar across the door. He closed the inside shutters to the one window.

This made the room dark, so he put more wood on the fire. He played with Jimmie until the child grew sleepy. Then Zeb undressed him and put him in the trundle bed.

He lay down by him so that Jimmie wouldn't miss Mother. By the time his brother was asleep, Zeb was sleepy himself. He tried to stay awake —he'd have to let his parents in. But it wouldn't matter if he closed his eyes a minute.

He wasn't sure it had been that long when he

heard a sort of pushing at the door. Then a panther screamed just outside. It sounded as if it were right at the door. Zeb was terrified. "It smelled the beef," he thought. "It will try to get in! It will push the door in!"

He wondered if King would drive it away. Then he remembered that King was locked in the barn every night with the stock. He was so frightened he could hear his heart pounding.

Thump-thump-knock-knock. He didn't know a heart could make so much noise. *Knock-knock-knock.* People were trying to talk to him, too. He could hardly hear for this thumping.

"Zeb! Zeb! Let us in! Zeb! Wake up! Zebulon! Wake up!"

Zeb woke up, jumped up, and opened the door. Mrs. Pike closed it behind them as Captain Pike put his gun on the mantel.

"How did you get along?" asked Mrs. Pike.

Zeb told his mother and father about the pan-

20

ther, but they said it was only a dream. They said he had been sound asleep when they came. They had had to knock and knock.

However, in the morning Captain Pike looked for panther tracks—and he found them! They were all around the cabin! The plainest and deepest tracks were at the door.

Varmints, Eagles and Wildcats

THE HUNTERS had tracked a panther from the Pike clearing to the ridge and had shot it. Now, one week later, the Captain had another worry. A neighbor had just come to warn him.

"I heard you were cutting down trees for a chicken house," said Mr. Joe Pierce. "I thought maybe I ought to give you some advice. Build your house tight, Captain. If you don't the varmints will get your chickens."

"They have already," replied Captain Pike. "We've missed several."

"It's hard to raise chickens here. Foxes, weasels, possums, and coons all just love chicken meat. We can't rightly call them thieves, either. They're just taking food that's easy to get."

"They won't find it easy to get into this henhouse," said Zeb. "I'm helping to build it."

"I see you are. I wish I had a boy to chop off the small branches from my logs."

"It's easy. My hatchet is sharp."

"Be careful you don't hit too hard. The hatchet might strike a knot and fly out of your hand. You or someone else might get hurt."

Zeb thought of this every time Jimmie came out to watch him. He would stop work and take his brother back to the cabin. It had happened twice this morning.

"You'll get hurt," Zeb had said each time. He had explained about the sharp hatchet, and Jimmie had seemed to understand. But here he was again. Zeb knew he had slipped out.

Zeb started back with him the third time. "I'm going to spank you," he said firmly.

24

"You can't," said Jimmie.

"Why can't I?"

"Because."

"Because why?"

"I'm a pet."

Zeb didn't want to laugh, but he had to. It was true, everyone petted Jimmie. He had never been strong. He was so thin Zeb said he could carry him and not know it. Therefore, instead of spanking the runaway, he hugged him and carried him to the cabin.

"I ran away, Mother," said Jimmie. He looked so cute and smiled so sweetly she hugged him, too. Zeb went back to his work, laughing.

He found three settlers talking to his father. They were on their way to the gristmill with corn. Zeb knew something was wrong, because they all looked very grave.

"We ought to do something about these bald eagles here," said Mr. White. "I saw one seize a baby pig of mine and fly away with it. I didn't have my gun, so I couldn't do anything."

"My baby pigs have been disappearing," said Mr. Pierce, "and my neighbor declared an eagle got his newborn lamb."

"Well, we can't blame the eagles," said Captain Pike. "The creek is dry, and they can't get any fish."

"That's true," Mr. Mason agreed. "But we can't afford to feed them and their young."

"Maybe we should afford it," argued Captain Pike. "The eagles are certainly helping us. For every pig and lamb, they'll seize a dozen rabbits and groundhogs. I don't need to tell you what these animals do to our crops."

Mr. White nodded. "They eat the corn blades as soon as they shoot above the ground. They eat other young vegetables, too."

Now Mr. Pierce nodded. "That's a fact. Besides, we won't have to feed eagles much longer.

The rains will come, the creek will be flowing, and there will be plenty of fish again."

"I wish I could see a bald eagle up close. Are they bald like old men?" asked Zeb.

"The young birds are at first. But the old birds aren't bald at all. They just seem to be from far away. Their heads and necks are covered with fine white feathers."

Now the men went on to the gristmill. Captain Pike rode with them with his bag of corn, and Zeb Pike went on working.

WILDCAT IN THE TREE

After an hour or so Zeb began to look at the sun. He thought it ought to be noon and dinnertime. Anyway, he was hungry even if the sun wasn't in the right place yet.

Then he saw his mother leave the cabin with her gun. He was astonished. She was always

27

cooking at this time. Another thing surprised him. She was almost running as she came toward him.

"Jimmie ran away!" she cried. "We must hunt for him. You take the trail up the creek, and I'll take the down trail."

"Has he been gone long?"

"I don't know. If he went into the forest, he's in danger. Go quickly, Zeb!"

In a short time Zeb was in the forest. There was only a dim light here. The sun couldn't shine through the mass of leaves and vines. It was hard to see the great thick roots that ran across the trail in places.

"Jimmie could stumble on these roots and break his leg," thought Zeb.

Suddenly he heard a dog barking. It wasn't far away, either. He hoped it was King, and he hoped Jimmie was with him.

The next minute Zeb hoped Jimmie wasn't

28

there. The dog was barking too fiercely. There was danger of some kind. He had never heard King bark like this but once. That was the day a wildcat was about to spring on a calf.

Zeb had followed his father to the pasture and had seen the "spitting" bobcat in the tree. He had examined it after his father had shot it. And he remembered its long sharp teeth and the strong sharp claws in its broad paws. He didn't like to think about them.

Zeb heard the dog growling now. The sound seemed to be close—just around the next bend in the trail. The boy stepped carefully as he hurried along on the thick mat of dead leaves.

At last he turned the bend. He was terrified by the sight he saw. There were King and Jimmie—and in a tree just across the trail was a huge wildcat! It was crouched to spring, and it was "spitting" angrily.

King was growling deep in his throat now and

showing his teeth. But little Jimmie was calling, "Kitty! Kitty! Kitty!"

"He doesn't know what it is," thought Zeb. "He thinks it's a tame pussycat. He doesn't know it could tear him to pieces."

By this time Zeb had reached his brother. He pushed Jimmie back against a tree and stood in front of him.

"The cat will have to attack me now," said Zeb to himself. Then he wondered whether he could fight the cat with its sharp teeth and claws.

King would try to fight the cat, of course. But the faithful pet wouldn't last long if the wild creature turned on him. Two dogs had been killed by bobcats just recently.

"If only Mother would come with her gun," Zeb thought. "If only I had some kind of weapon! If—why, I have! My hatchet! I had forgotten I was still carrying it." The next instant it was sailing through the air.

31

The hatchet hit the cat's head, and the animal fell to the ground, dead.

Zeb patted King and told him he was a brave dog. King understood and licked Zeb's hand. But Jimmie cried. "I wanted it for a pet," he said. "I wanted to take it home."

Zeb didn't argue. He just picked up Jimmie and carried him along the trail.

Fun in the Wilderness

"MOTHER, ZEB won't play with me," complained Jimmie one day.

"I don't feel like playing," Zeb explained.

"Aren't you well?"

"I'm all right, Mother. I just don't want to play right now."

Mrs. Pike understood. Zeb had been playing baby games with his little brother all winter. He needed a playmate of his own age, and there wasn't one on the creek.

Captain Pike agreed with her.

"Zeb is over nine years old now," he said. "He's too old for Jimmie's games. I've been hoping a new family would move into this neigh-borhood. I've been hoping they'd have a boy around nine."

"I've been wishing the same thing myself."

The wish came true the following week. Mr. Thomas Ryan arrived with his family, including twin boys about Zeb's age. They were to live near by. Mr. Ryan's land joined Captain Pike's.

Zeb was delighted. There was one trouble, however. He couldn't tell the boys apart. He never knew whether he was talking with Dave or Dan.

The three boys had fun all summer and fall. They went fishing and swimming. They picked wild strawberries in June. They went after blackberries in July. In August they found wild gooseberries and wished they hadn't after they ate too many.

In September the three friends picked wild grapes and swung on the vines. In October they feasted on papaws and persimmons. Then in November they gathered nuts.

In between times they were learning to shoot with bows and arrows. Their fathers showed them how to stand and hold their bows. They made them practice a long time on taking an arrow from the quiver.

When late fall came, the boys wanted to go hunting. But Mr. Ryan said they couldn't. "Each one of you missed the target this morning."

"Only once!" cried Dan.

"That once would mean three animals wounded instead of killed."

Therefore, the target practice went on until both fathers were completely satisfied. Then came a light snow with rabbit tracks running everywhere. That morning the three hunters were ready for their first hunt.

Now Captain Pike laid down the law. "You are not to go on the ridge. You must stay close to clearings. If you disobey and go deep into the forest, this will be your last hunt, Zeb."

"It will be your last hunt, too," Mr. Ryan told the twins.

The boys didn't disobey. They knew the dangers in the deep forest. They found plenty of small game near their own clearings. Their families feasted on squirrels, rabbits, possums, wild ducks, and sometimes wild turkeys.

Winter came with cold winds and deep snow. The game animals hid in caves and burrows. The hunters had to stay in their cabins. But it was a fine time to crack nuts and eat them before the blazing logs in the fireplace.

THE MYSTERIOUS WAGON

Zeb didn't have a chance to get lonely, for he was going to school. The cabin was his schoolroom, and Father was his teacher. Captain Pike couldn't work outside now, and Mrs. Pike was busy with cooking and weaving.

There had never been a school in the settlement. Zeb hadn't read a line since he left Master Walls's pay school in Bucks County. But Master Pike was surprised the first morning.

His pupil couldn't read, spell, or add. He could hardly write his name. "You've forgotten everything you ever knew," the master said. "You must study every afternoon."

Zeb really tried, but he was always glad when there was company. His mother said it wasn't polite to study then.

This afternoon Mr. White came. He said he had waded through deep snow, but he had important news for Captain Pike. "I learned this from a traveler at the blacksmith's. He had heard it in a settlement near Pittsburgh."

"That's almost in Indian country," said Captain Pike.

"It's so close the settlers living there watch every traveler passing through. Not long ago they found a man with a wagonload of guns."

"For Indians?" asked Mrs. Pike.

"Yes, Ma'am—guns for Indians."

"I'm glad the settlers caught the rascal," said Captain Pike.

"They burned his wagon and load."

"Good!" exclaimed Mrs. Pike.

"That's not all. The settlers made the rascal talk. He said there was another wagon on the way. He said this one was loaded with hatchets, knives, lead, and gunpowder."

"I'd like to catch the driver of that wagon!" exclaimed Captain Pike.

"Well, Captain, the people around here are counting on you to get him. I told them you were a spy for General Washington in the War for Independence."

"A spy! Father, were you a spy?" asked Zeb.

"He was, lad, and there wasn't a better one in the whole army," said Mr. White. "Your father was the General's favorite spy."

"Oh, come now, Mr. White," said the Captain. "You're stretching things a bit. Besides, you're getting Zeb excited."

"He'll see real excitement, Captain, when you catch that rascal."

"I'll do my best to capture him."

"Let me know. I want to see the fireworks."

As soon as Mr. White was gone, Zeb told his parents some real news. "I'm going to be a spy for the army when I'm old enough."

"You'll have to read a whole lot better than you do now," said his father.

"Does a spy have to read?"

"An army spy has to read the enemy's messages, orders, and letters. He has to read fast or he might be caught."

"Did the British ever catch you?"

"I wouldn't be here if they had."

"I meant, did they almost catch you?"

"Oh, they almost caught me several times. But I had read their papers every time."

"Your father was a good spy, because he could read fast," said Mrs. Pike.

"I'll learn to read fast, too," said Zeb. "I'll study every afternoon—honest I will."

By spring Zeb was reading very well. He was fair in spelling, good in arithmetic, and his writing was very good.

School was out. There would be no more lessons till the next winter. There was a garden to spade and a field to plow and seeds to plant.

The twins were busy helping their father. When they weren't working the three boys played together. Today Zeb had a chance to visit his friends. The minute he saw them he knew they had something important to tell him.

"Hello, Dan. Hello, Dave," said Zeb.

"Hello, Zeb," the twins said together.

"Zeb, a new settler has moved into that old cabin near our pasture," said Dan.

"There's a boy our age, but his father wouldn't let us play with him. He told us to go home and stay there," said Dan.

"We were just standing there looking at his big wagon," said Dave. "We wanted to see what the man had in it."

"He hadn't unloaded," Dan added. "He kept the cover tied down all the time."

"That's queer," Zeb said.

"He drives his children away if they play around it," said Dave. "I heard him say someone was coming for the load and he'd whip them if they touched the cover."

"For goodness' sakes!" Zeb exclaimed. "I wonder if he's the man the settlers are looking for? You know, that man with a wagonload of weapons and gunpowder for Indians."

41

"Oh!" cried the astonished twins.

"Maybe he's waiting here for some Indian to come after the load."

"Sure he is, Zeb! Sure he is! Why didn't we think of that, Dave?"

"I don't know, Dan."

"Go home and tell your father!" cried Zeb. "I'm going to tell mine."

Then Zeb ran one way and the Ryan twins ran another.

Almost before Zeb had finished, Captain Pike was putting the saddle on his horse. "I think you are right about that load, Zeb. I'll tell the settlers. Look out for a fire tonight."

"May I go over there?"

"It will be no place for boys. You have done your share, and so have the twins. I shall give you three boys the credit if this proves to be the man we're looking for."

He mounted now, but he spoke to Zeb again.

"You did some quick thinking, son. Maybe you will make an army spy." He smiled and saluted Zeb as he rode away.

That night there were fireworks and an explosion, too. At sunrise the strange man and family drove away in their cart, and a dozen armed settlers watched them go.

For and Against a Crown

THAT SPRING, 1789, many new settlers came with their families. They cleared land, built cabins, and planted crops.

There were now enough children in the settlement for a school, so their fathers built one from logs. This was hard work, but not so hard as finding a teacher. Several men had refused.

"They don't want to come away out here to the wilderness," said a pioneer mother. "I guess they're afraid of wild animals."

"Perhaps they are old and can't stand the long trip," said another mother. "We'll probably have to find a young man."

Finally a teacher was found. He was young Louis Faraway from faraway New York City. He liked the trip, and he loved the beautiful scenery of the Bald Eagle Creek country. But he had a hard time with his pupils at first.

He couldn't get them interested in their lessons. They were all excited over some news they had heard. General George Washington had just become President of the United States!

Every ex-soldier on the creek was delighted. The people talked about the news at home and their children talked about it at school. Every day the teacher answered a dozen questions.

"No, President Washington won't live in Great Britain like King George. America doesn't belong to Great Britain now."

"No, the President won't keep soldiers in every town to make people obey him."

"No, a trumpeter will not walk ahead of the President when he goes out."

"No, he won't wear a velvet robe like a King. He'll dress like an American gentleman."

Master Faraway never laughed at any question, no matter how foolish it was. He understood. These children couldn't see the difference between a President and a King.

Today the Ryan twins had raised their hands. The master nodded.

"Will the President live in a palace?" asked Dave. "Will he sit on a throne and wear a gold crown on his head?"

"Will he make people kneel to him?" asked Dan. "Will he put them in prison if they don't?"

"Zeb, you may answer those questions. Your father fought under General Washington and knew him well. I suppose he has told you the kind of a man the General was?"

"Yes, sir, he has. I know General Washington wouldn't live in a palace, and he wouldn't sit on a throne with a crown on his head. He wouldn't make people kneel, either. He didn't like Kings. He wouldn't try to act like one."

Boys laughed and clapped.

Then Zeb went on. "Didn't General Washington fight a long war to get rid of the King we had? He won, too!"

Again boys laughed and clapped. But the twins didn't. They looked pretty glum.

Zeb was puzzled. He had been sure they would agree with him. He told his parents about it as soon as he got home.

"Mr. Ryan might be a Tory," said Captain Pike, "and all Tories wanted the English King to rule over America."

"The Ryans came from New Jersey," said Mrs. Pike. "There were many Tories there."

"I came from New Jersey, too," said Zeb. "But I'm not a Tory. I'm a patriot."

"You were born there," said his mother. "You were only three years old when we moved to

Bucks County, Pennsylvania. You didn't know much about Tories then."

"You didn't know much about patriots, either," his father added, smiling. "You'd better not say anything more to the twins, Zeb. It might make trouble."

Zeb didn't say any more, but the twins said plenty to him the next morning at recess.

"Pa said a President ought to wear a crown," said Dan.

"Pa said no one would mind him if he didn't," said Dave.

"You couldn't get a crown on George Washington's head," Zeb declared.

"You could too!"

"You couldn't!"

"You could!" shouted the "Crown boys."

"You couldn't!" shouted soldiers' sons.

The next instant the yard was a mass of angry boys. They pushed and shoved and shouted and yelled. The master heard them in the school-room and came running quickly.

The commotion stopped at once. But Master Faraway knew there would be more trouble as soon as his back was turned.

RINGLEADER ZEB

There was so much trouble the teacher had to separate the two groups. The "Crown boys" played in one end of the yard. The "No-Crowns" played in the other end.

In spite of this a new pupil managed to make trouble. He was fourteen-year-old Lester Mills. He picked on younger boys when the master wasn't looking. He threatened to fight them if they joined the "No-Crowns." He did, too, after school was out.

Almost every day parents came to the school to complain about him. Two women were here

now. They said Lester had hurt their sons who were only six and seven years old.

"Did this happen on the school grounds?"

"No, Master, it was on the way home."

"I'm afraid I can't do anything about it then. I've been to see the bully's parents, but they upheld him. They said the schoolboys picked on Lester because he was poor."

"That's ridiculous! We're all poor here."

"I think I'll see the sheriff about that boy, before some other child is hurt," said the teacher.

After the women left Master Faraway was busy for some time with schoolwork. He was just leaving when Captain Pike came. "We were worried about Zeb," he said. "He didn't come home. Did you keep him in?"

"No, sir. He left with the others an hour ago."

"An hour! Then he's had trouble. He always comes straight home. Have you any idea where I might look for him?"

"I have a very good idea. I believe Lester Mills will know. He has threatened to fight Zeb several times. Other boys have told me."

"Has Zeb been fighting him?"

"Zeb hasn't fought anyone. But he's the ring-leader of the No-Crown boys. That's all the excuse Lester needs."

"I'll go to the Mills cabin at once."

"I'll go with you. I'll get my gun."

In a short time the schoolmaster and Captain Pike were in the Mills cabin. They asked Lester about Zeb, but he declared he didn't know where Zeb was.

"Didn't he tell you where he was going?" asked Captain Pike.

"I didn't see him after school."

"You must have seen him," said the master. "You left at the same time."

"Why don't you let the boy alone?" Mrs. Mills asked. "He told you he didn't know anything."

"He isn't telling the truth. There's Zeb's reader on your table!"

Captain Pike took up the book and looked at it. "It is Zeb's! Here's his name inside. How did you get it?"

Lester looked at his mother quickly. "He found it," she replied.

"Where did you find it?"

Again the boy looked at his mother.

"Your mother's not going to answer this time," Captain Pike said sternly, "and if you don't tell the truth, you'll spend this night in jail. The sheriff isn't far away."

Lester was scared now. "I'll tell you. He's tied up—in a cave."

"With wild animals roaming about!" cried Captain Pike.

"I didn't think about them. But you can get there quickly. It isn't far. It's in the cliff on this side of the creek. You can find it easily."

54

"You can, too, young man, and you're starting now," said the Captain angrily.

"I didn't know this," said Mrs. Mills. "I thought there had just been a fight."

The men didn't reply. They followed Lester from the cabin and along the bank to a cliff. The boy stopped at an opening in the rock wall. "He's in there," he said.

"Zeb!" called Captain Pike. "Zeb!"

Out of the dark shadows of the cave came a faint cry. "Father!"

Captain Pike and Master Faraway found Zeb on the ground, helpless. While the teacher stood guard, the Captain cut the boy's ropes.

"I can walk," said Zeb. "I'm all right. Lester hid and waited for me. Then he struck me from behind. I didn't have a chance to fight him. He tried to make me say that President Washington wanted a crown, but I wouldn't."

"Lester will pay for this," said the Captain.

"He can't come to my school another day," said Master Faraway.

Lester was gone when Zeb and the two men came from the cave.

"Let him go," Captain Pike said. "The sheriff will get him tomorrow."

But the Mills's cabin was empty the next day. All the sheriff found was Zeb's reader.

The Favorite Game

THE NEXT day everyone knew what had happened to Zeb. Parents were alarmed now about their own sons.

"No more fights," they said.

"No more groups," the master said. "You're all Americans here. You'll play together, or you won't play at all—you'll study at recess."

That settled it. In no time all the pupils were friends again. They were still asking questions, however. But these were about George Washington's great battles in the War for Independence.

Their favorite story was about the battle he

won at Trenton, New Jersey. They asked for it over and over. They liked it so much they made up a game about it. They called it "Washington Crossing the Delaware."

There was only one trouble. Everyone wanted to be Washington, so the master persuaded them to take turns. Today it was Zeb's turn.

The Delaware River had been marked on the playground. It ran through the center. On one side was Pennsylvania. On the other was New Jersey. Trenton was behind the woodpile.

The British troops were in camp there. General Washington's army of patriots was camped on the Pennsylvania shore.

Master Faraway liked this game himself. So today he helped to start it. "Now, boys," he said, "remember it's Christmas Day. It is very cold. There is snow on the ground, and there is ice in the Delaware River. Try to act cold, please. Shiver and rub your hands together."

"We can't do that, Master!" cried Patriot Dan Ryan. "We have to carry our guns."

"That's right—you do carry cornstalks for guns," said Master Faraway.

"We could warm up one hand at a time," Patriot Dave Ryan suggested. "We could just shake each hand good and hard."

"That's fine," said the schoolmaster. "General Washington, take your army to the Pennsylvania shore. Henry, take your British soldiers over to your camp—over behind the woodpile. Ready! You speak first, Zeb."

General Washington pointed to the woodpile. "Our enemies are over there across the Delaware River," he shouted. "This should be a good time to capture them. I see our boats are almost ready. Come with me, men."

"But, General," said an officer, "the river is full of floating ice. The boats can't possibly get through to the other side."

"We must get through! We'll never have a better chance to capture the British. They won't be expecting us on account of this ice. We'll take them by surprise."

"Their sentries will hear the oars in the oarlocks," protested another officer. "They will warn their camp. We'll be shot as we land."

"There won't be any sentries tonight, Captain. Their officers will be at Christmas parties in Trenton. The soldiers will be stuffing themselves with turkey and plum pudding."

"Can't we wait till the river freezes over?" asked a young officer. "Then we could walk across and capture them."

"Then they would walk across and capture us," the General replied sternly. "They have more men, more guns, more powder than we have. We couldn't even fight them."

"The boats are ready, General Washington!" a boatman called.

"Into your boats, men!" shouted the General. "I'm getting into mine!"

Zeb pretended to climb into a boat. Four rowers followed him. The troops climbed into boats. The General stood up. "Row, men, row!" he shouted. "Row!"

"Aye, aye!" shouted the rowers. They pretended to row.

"Faster!" shouted Washington. "Faster!"

"I can't row any faster, sir," said one soldier. "My oars freeze to the ice."

"So do mine, sir," said another.

"It is sleeting, sir!" shouted rower Dan.

"It is hailing, sir!" shouted rower Dave.

"Pay no attention to sleet! Never mind the hail!" shouted the General. "We're almost there. Now we are there! Out of the boats, men!"

All pretended to climb out of boats.

"Did you keep your powder and guns dry?" the General asked.

"Yes, sir!" shouted all the soldiers in the patriot army.

"Then follow me to the enemy's camp!"

He led his troops to the woodpile. "Go in and capture them! Take them by surprise!"

The patriots rushed behind the woodpile. A moment later they came out with many British soldiers as prisoners.

"Aha!" cried General Washington. "You fellows didn't expect us, did you?"

"No, sir."

"You didn't think we could cross the river, did you?"

"No, sir."

"Did you think that ice would scare me?"

"Yes, sir."

"What has your leader to say?"

"I say you're a brave and smart general."

"I promised my men I'd capture you and your force. I always keep my word."

"We know you do, General. We know all about your little hatchet and the cherry tree."

"Ha, ha!" laughed General Washington.

"Ha, ha!" laughed his troops.

"Ha, ha!" laughed the enemy.

The school bell rang. The noon recess was over, and patriots and enemy went in together.

Zeb's First Gun and Bear

On January fifth, 1791, Zebulon Montgomery Pike was twelve years old. The weather was bitterly cold. Deep snow covered the ground. The creek was frozen over, and long icicles hung down from the cabin roof.

Zeb saw his own breath while he was dressing. He was shivering as he went down the ladder from the loft. But the minute he saw his birthday present he felt warm all over.

The present was something he had wanted for a long time, ever since he was nine. But his father had said he'd have to wait till he was twelve. Here it was at last—a gun!

"It's beautiful!" Zeb cried. "I was afraid you wouldn't give it to me."

"Frontier boys should have guns when they are twelve," said his father. "They are old enough then to hunt small game. They can help to keep the family in meat."

"We'll need more meat now," said Mrs. Pike. "Jimmie is seven. Baby Maria is two."

"I'll bring in enough for all of us," declared Zeb. "You won't need to hunt at all, Father."

"I'll be glad of that," said the Captain. "I need more time for farm work."

Zeb couldn't bear to put his gun down while he ate breakfast. He wanted to hold it on his lap.

"No, you'll forget to eat," Mrs. Pike said, and she leaned the gun in a corner.

Zeb couldn't keep his eyes from the beautiful thing. He missed his mouth three times and dropped mush on the table. He was looking at it now as he reached for his mug of milk.

"Mother, Zeb spilled his milk all over me!" cried Jimmie.

Mrs. Pike put the gun under bedcovers. But this didn't help things at all, for now Zeb talked about his gun so much he didn't have time to eat. When breakfast was over and he left the table, his bowl was half full of mush.

"I thought I'd show you how to use your gun this morning," said his father. "But we'll have to wait till it's warmer."

"It doesn't seem cold to me."

"It's down to zero."

"I'd like to show my gun to the twins. They brought their guns over here on their birthday."

"That was back in May," said his mother. "The grass was green, flowers were blooming, and birds were singing."

"Ha, ha!" laughed Captain Pike.

Zeb wouldn't even smile. "The twins won't like it if I don't."

"You're not going anywhere, except to the barn and woodpile," his father said firmly.

Zeb helped feed the stock and carry in wood and water. Captain Pike said he was nearly frozen, but Zeb wouldn't admit he was cold.

After dinner Captain Pike showed him how to load his gun. The boy practiced until his father was satisfied. Zeb was delighted.

"Now I can get them, Jimmie!" he cried.

"Bears?"

"Of course!" Zeb bragged.

"Of course!" exclaimed Mrs. Pike with a laugh. "I speak for your first bearskin. I want to put it by my bed. It would be nice to step on these cold mornings."

"I'll get one for you, Mother," said Zeb. He meant it, too.

"I was joking, son. You're not old enough to hunt bears. Isn't that right, Father?"

"Indeed it is!" said Captain Pike. "Only a

very good hunter should go bear-hunting. One bullet won't kill a bear unless it hits in just the right spot."

"I know," declared Zeb. "Mr. White told me. The bullet has to hit the bear either in the heart or in the ear."

"If a hunter misses with his first shot, the bear will be clawing him before he can reload," the Captain added. "You see, Zeb, you'll have to grow up before you can go on a bear hunt."

"But I might meet one when I wasn't hunting," said Zeb.

"If you see one, don't wait to take aim," said his father. "Just run!"

"Bears can run faster than men," said Jimmie.

"That's true, but they can't run so fast downhill as they can on level ground. Look for a hill. If you don't see one close by, climb the nearest tree."

"Bears can climb trees," said Jimmie.

"They can climb only on the heavy limbs," said the Captain. "Zeb could go all the way to the top where a bear couldn't climb."

"It could stretch out and drag him down," said Jimmie.

"Where did you learn all about bears?" asked the boys' mother.

"We learned at school," answered Jimmie. "Master Faraway taught us."

"Every frontier boy should learn the habits of wild animals," said Captain Pike. "But you boys won't be meeting bears around here any more. Several hunters have told me that the bears have left this part of the country."

"Why would they leave?" asked Zeb.

"Well, I suppose there are too many clearings and people to suit them," said the Captain.

"Maybe they'll come back," said Jimmie.

"I hope so," said Zeb. "If they do, I can save a skin for you, Mother."

"I want you to save your own skin, Zeb. I hope they'll never come back."

THE MARKSMAN

The cold weather lasted some time, but there were nice days now and then. On the first one, Zeb went to the Ryan cabin with his gun. The twins examined it carefully.

"It's a good gun," Dan declared at last.

"It's a good gun," Dave said firmly.

Zeb was pleased. If the twins said a gun was good, it was. Then the boys made plans for a big hunt as soon as the weather was warmer. They would sleep one night in the forest, and they'd stalk a deer.

Zeb practiced shooting every day. When it rained he shot at a target from the barn door.

Then one day his father said Zeb was a pretty good marksman. "You are ready to hunt now, Zeb," he added.

"Could I go today? The rain has stopped and the sun is out."

"You might get us a wild duck for dinner. Your mother wants one to bake."

"I won't have time to go for the twins, will I?"

"No, not if you like baked duck."

Zeb started out along the creek. Other hunters were out, too. The boy heard gunfire. Then suddenly he heard something crashing through the brush behind him. He thought it was a hunter and turned to look.

A great black bear was coming toward him! Now it saw him and growled fiercely. There was no time to take aim and shoot. There was no large tree near—nothing but saplings.

There was no hill. But the creek bank was steep. It would slow the bear up if it followed him. He could hear it growling as he scrambled down the bank to the shore.

He looked back—the bear had started down the bank! It was following him! If he ran it would overtake him. He had to face the beast and try to kill it. He waited till it came closer, then he aimed at its ear and fired.

There was an instant when Zeb didn't know what would happen. He was so frightened he was weak. Then the bear fell! He had hit the right spot! He started toward it—and stopped. It might not be dead!

Zeb ran all the way home. He was so excited he could hardly talk when he got there. Finally his parents understood.

"Well, Mother," said Captain Pike, "you'll have a bearskin rug before long."

"I'm sorry I didn't get a duck for dinner, Mother."

"Who is thinking of ducks?" said his mother. "We'll have bear steak, Zeb."

Captain Pike praised Zeb for his fine marksmanship. "You'll make a real frontiersman, son."

"I think he's one now," Mrs. Pike said fondly.

The Secret
Mission

THE SPRING of 1791 came at last. Grass was green and wild flowers bloomed. Zeb was picking violets for his baby sister Maria this morning. He had almost enough for a bouquet when he suddenly stopped.

Two soldiers were hitching their horses near the gate. Zeb saw them salute his father and follow him into the cabin. Violets in hand, Zeb hurried to the cabin. He was in time to hear their names—Lieutenant Dixon and Sergeant Nash.

When they were all seated Lieutenant Dixon explained to Captain Pike. "We belong to the army troops stationed at Carlisle, Pennsylvania.

We bring you a message from our commanding officer, Colonel Thompson. It is a secret matter."

Mrs. Pike stood. "I'll take the boys outside, Lieutenant."

"Please stay, Madam. You will have to know anyway. But the boys——"

"The older one can be trusted with any secret," said Captain Pike. "The younger one might talk at the wrong time."

"Jimmie," said Mrs. Pike, "don't you want to play outside?"

Jimmie shook his head.

"How would you like to help me with my saddlebags?" the sergeant asked.

The little boy liked this idea. He took the soldier's hand and went out with him.

The Lieutenant continued, "Captain Pike, this message really came from President Washington. He wrote Colonel Thompson about your work as a spy in the War of the Revolution."

"But why? I don't understand?"

"Well, he wishes you to take up this same work again."

"There is no enemy to spy on," said the Captain. "There is no war."

"The President is afraid there will be a war—a terrible one. The Indian tribes in the Ohio River country are getting ready to go on the warpath against white settlers. What's more, they are getting guns from somewhere."

"Then the poor settlers won't have a chance," said Mrs. Pike. "They might defend themselves against arrows, but not against guns."

"Who is supplying these guns, Lieutenant?" asked the Captain.

"That is what you are to find out, sir. Colonel Thompson had a little information about the gun seller. A Mr. William MacFeeters, a fur trader, is suspected. He owns a large trading post in New York State near Lake Erie."

"It's a good place for gun trading," said Captain Pike. "Indian runners could take them down into the Ohio country to the tribes there."

"Exactly. There is an Indian camp near the trading post."

"The runners probably live there."

"That's what the Colonel thought."

"I wish I could investigate that camp and the trader, but it might take a long time. I couldn't leave my family."

"They could live in the fort at Carlisle."

"I have a better plan," said Mrs. Pike. "We can live with the Ryans. They have been wanting us ever since Mrs. Ryan came down with ague. She really needs me, Zebulon."

"That's true, but she doesn't need four boys. That's too many for a sick woman."

"There would be only three if I could go with you," said Zeb. "That wouldn't be too many, would it? She wouldn't mind the twins and——"

78

"I'd take care of Jimmie and Maria," Mrs. Pike added with a smile.

"Why not take the boy, Captain? The Colonel said you could take a companion. He sent money for such expenses."

"There might not be a good place for him to stay while I'm away scouting."

"You could leave him at the trading post. It would be a safe place. It has a high stockade like a fort, and there are cabins inside for trappers and travelers."

"The owners would expect a price to put him up, of course."

"Of course. But you'll have money. The sergeant is guarding it now, in my saddlebags."

"It would make a good headquarters."

"I wouldn't be afraid while you were away, Father," said Zeb.

"What do you think about it, Isabella?"

"I think you should help to find the man selling guns to the Indians. Anyway, I think it will be wonderful for Zeb. He will travel through new country. He will see the great trading post and beautiful furs. I'd like to go myself."

"Well, then, I'll go on this mission, Lieutenant. I'll take my son with me, too."

GUARDING THE MONEYBAG

That evening, after Jimmie was asleep, Captain Pike talked to the others gravely. "We can't tell anyone the real reason for my journey. It would cause talk."

"Of course," Mrs. Pike agreed. "Everyone would be excited."

Captain Pike nodded. "Hunters would be sure to repeat it, and Indians might hear. Then we wouldn't live to get to the post."

"What can I tell the boys, Father?" asked Zeb. "They'll all ask me."

"Say that I am going north to look into the fur business—and that I may quit farming. This is what I shall tell the men."

"Well, that's true," said Mrs. Pike. "I've heard you say that many times. But people will wonder how you can afford the trip. You might stop at an inn on the way—and there are the cabin and meals at the post."

"Tell them I sold part of our farm. This is true also. The Lieutenant bought a strip today."

"For himself?"

"Yes, after he leaves the army. There is one more thing—I must leave in one week."

Now the busy week was almost over. Yesterday the twins had helped Zeb take the chickens to their place. Today Zeb had driven three cows there by himself.

Saddlebags had been packed. Bedrolls were ready for the pack horse. Also bundles of clothing and bags of food were ready.

At last the day came. The wagon was waiting to take Mother, Maria, and Jimmie to the Ryan cabin. Their bundles of clothing and bedding were inside. They had told Zeb good-by and had climbed to the driver's seat.

Mrs. Pike was drying her eyes, and Zeb was wiping his. Captain Pike lifted the reins. Then he dropped them. "Zeb," he said, "you'll be here alone for a while. You'll have to guard that bag of money. Don't let any stranger in."

"I won't. But how would anyone know the Lieutenant gave it to you?"

"They knew he was here and bought the land. There'll be talk about it at the mill."

"I won't let anyone in. Good-by, Mother! Good-by, Jimmie! Good-by, Maria!"

"Good-by, Zeb! Good-by, Zeb!"

When they were out of sight Zeb went to the cabin. It looked empty without Mother and the children. His eyes filled with tears again.

Suddenly he heard a slight noise outside. It sounded like the squeaking of leather. It couldn't be Father's saddle. He was to leave the wagon and ride a horse back. But he couldn't get back from the Ryans' this soon.

Zeb opened the door and looked out. He had been right—a saddle had squeaked. A strange

man was hitching his horse to the post near the gate. Suddenly the boy was afraid.

The stranger was coming into the yard, and he carried a gun. Zeb thought of the bag of money hidden in his father's saddlebags.

"Hey, you" called the man. "Can you give me some food?"

Zeb shut the door and barred it. He closed the shutters. He took his own gun from the mantel.

"Hey, you," called the man again. "I'll pay for what I eat."

Zeb didn't answer.

Now the man was right at the door. "You needn't be afraid of me, lad. I've got a boy of my own about your age. He's not afraid of strangers. He'd open the door for anyone who was hungry."

Zeb didn't answer.

Then the man shouted angrily, "If you know what's good for you, you'll open the door!"

Zeb was silent.

"I'll make you sorry for this—you and your father, both!"

Presently Zeb heard the squeaking of saddle leather, but he was too smart to look out. The man might be pretending to leave, so the boy stood by the door with his gun in his hands until he heard his father's voice.

Riding the
North Trail

"OF COURSE that man was after the money," said Captain Pike. "He may try to waylay us. But we'll be ready for him."

The Captain cautioned Zeb while they were loading the pack horse. "You must keep up with me. Don't stop to look at bird nests and flowers. Watch bushes. They might be moving, and there's no wind today."

"Do you mean the stranger could be hiding behind them?" asked Zeb.

"Yes. Also listen for the sound of snapping twigs. They don't snap by themselves."

Then the Captain and his son mounted and

took the north trail along Bald Eagle Creek. Zeb rode behind his father, leading the pack horse. Man and boy carried guns and watched and listened. At noon they stopped to eat.

Captain Pike was sure they were safe now. "The stranger wouldn't come this far to waylay us," he said.

"Maybe he heard how quick you are with a trigger," put in Zeb.

"Maybe he heard that you are pretty good yourself. Anyway, the man probably didn't want to tackle the two of us."

After the horses were watered, Zeb tied them in a grassy place with long grazing ropes. He was proud of these ropes. He had made them himself from strips of deerhide. "The horses can get plenty of grass," he said.

"They can thank you for that. Now we must keep our guns handy while we eat. Some animal might smell our fresh meat."

They had just finished when they heard a queer noise in the distance. They jumped to their feet and reached for their guns.

"What is it?" asked Zeb. "There it is again!"

"It's too far away. I can't tell."

Zeb and his father waited. Now the noise was nearer, and they knew what it was. They laughed and put their guns down.

A farmer riding a horse came around a bend. A baby pig was buttoned up under his coat. Only its head showed. It was squirming and squealing.

The farmer stopped. "I'm taking it to my little boy for a pet. But I'm afraid I'll never get it home. It's mighty squirmy."

"It's cute," said Zeb.

"It's a squealer. Where are you bound?"

"I want to see that sawmill up the creek," Captain Pike replied.

"Are you looking for work there?"

"Are men needed?"

"I heard they were, but I don't know myself. I don't travel that way. It's too close to Indian country to suit me."

"Isn't it a day's ride from here?"

"It's more like two. Well, good day to you both and good luck!"

The farmer rode away, and Zeb smiled at his father. "You didn't tell him a thing. You didn't tell him a story either. We do want to see that sawmill."

"A spy can't tell his plans to just anyone, son," the Captain said with a laugh.

Late that afternoon the travelers found a deserted cabin. They carried their things in and made a fire in the fireplace. Zeb warmed some meat and corncakes in a frying pan.

He had the supper ready when his father came in from looking after the horses. The boy was so tired he could hardly eat.

"It isn't any fun to ride a horse all day, is it, Zeb?" asked the Captain.

"I'm not tired—that is, not very tired."

"Well, I am. I'm going to sleep now."

"Then I will, too."

Zeb and his father rolled up in blankets and lay on the floor near the fire. In one minute they were both sound asleep.

HOMESICK AND BASHFUL

The second night out, the travelers had to sleep on the ground. Zeb was too weary to care. He was so stiff he could hardly walk. He was sore all over. Even his face ached. He couldn't say one word when his father talked about Mother and Jimmie and Maria.

Captain Pike knew Zeb was saddlesore, but he thought the boy was also homesick. He had never been away from home before.

Captain Pike was glad when he saw a covered wagon coming during their noon rest the following day. He hoped there would be a boy Zeb could play with. But there was a young girl on the driver's seat with a man and woman.

"These people will stop. Then you can talk with the girl, Zeb," he said.

"I don't talk much with girls," said Zeb.

"Oh, of course not!" The Captain smiled.

The driver stopped his team and spoke. "We are bound for the Bald Eagle Creek settlement. Do you know anything about it, sir?"

"I should," said the Captain. "I live there."

The man jumped from the wagon at once. His wife and daughter followed.

"Lucy," said the woman, "go over and talk with the boy. He's about your age. Ask him his name and tell him yours."

The pretty girl obeyed, and the woman turned to Captain Pike. "I wanted to get her away," she said in a low voice. "There are things I want to ask you about the settlement. I didn't want her to hear."

"Well, we have a school, and we are going to build a church this fall."

"That's splendid. But I want to know something else. Is there any danger of an Indian attack? Have any cabins been burned? Have any settlers been killed?"

"No, Madam," replied the Captain. "The Indians sold all their land and left. I haven't seen one since we moved there four years ago."

"Thank goodness! We had to leave our settlement. The Indians were about to attack us."

"We lived across the border in New York State," the man explained. "Our settlement wasn't far from MacFeeters' trading post."

"We got away just in time," declared the woman. "Some of the Indians have guns."

"Where did they get them?"

"I don't know. Our hunters saw them though. That's all I know," said the woman as she climbed up to the wagon seat.

The man walked away, out of her sight. Then he beckoned to Captain Pike to join him.

"I feel I should explain," the man said softly. "There wasn't any danger. My wife just got scared. She heard a lot of talk."

"Was it just talk—about the guns?"

"Oh no! That part was true. Several hunters told about seeing Indians with guns."

"Was there talk about where the savages got the guns?"

"Everyone thought they came from the trading post—Mr. MacFeeters' place, that is."

"Why does everyone think this?"

"MacFeeters is getting rich—too quick."

The men went on talking. Zeb wanted to join them, but he didn't know how to get away from Lucy. She was talking about his name now.

"It's a funny name. Zeboo—I can't say it."
She giggled, and Zeb blushed.

"I don't think it's funny," he managed to say.

"What would Indians do if they captured
you? They couldn't say your name, could they?"
She giggled again.

Zeb thought she was making fun of him. He
had a good notion to pull her yellow braids. It
would be easy to give them a good yank.

94

"Why don't you talk with me?"

"I don't know what to say."

"Would you try to save me if an Indian got after me with a tomahawk?"

"No."

"Why wouldn't you?"

"I'd be running the other way."

"You don't like me, do you?"

"I—I guess not—— I mean, I guess so."

"I like you. I think you're pretty."

Zeb's face turned scarlet. She was making fun of him again. He reached for her braids——

"Come, Lucy!" called her mother. "We're going now!"

"Good-by, Zeboo!"

Zeb didn't answer. He walked off and looked the other way.

Captain Pike waved his hat to the folks from New York State. He was surprised at his son's bad manners. "Lucy is waving to you, Zeb."

"I don't care. Let her wave."

"Why, I thought she was a sweet little girl."

"Sweet! Humph! She said I was pretty!"

"She did? My, my! I'm surprised."

"I don't like girls talking that way to me."

"Of course not! Certainly not! I don't blame you." Then the Captain went down to the creek so Zeb wouldn't hear him laugh.

Bad Night at Loggers' Inn

THE TWO TRAVELERS followed Bald Eagle Creek for two more days. They were still on its bank when they reached the sawmill.

Zeb had expected to see the great mill wheel churning the water and moving the big saw. He had wanted to watch the saw slice the thick logs into strips of lumber.

But the boy was disappointed. The great wheel wasn't turning. The saw wasn't moving. Not a single man was working.

A guard at the mill explained. "It was quitting time half an hour ago. The men have gone to a loggers' inn for supper."

"Will the landlord take in travelers?" asked Captain Pike.

"He will if he has room for them. You had better hurry, though, or you'll be caught in a storm. The inn is near the logging camp. It's about a mile upstream."

The clouds were black and a strong wind was blowing when the travelers reached the loggers' inn. The landlord was sorry, but every room was filled. Every bed was filled, too.

"There are three men in each bed," he explained. "There's only the floor left."

"Well, Zeb, the floor will be better than the ground if it rains," said the Captain.

Two loggers now came up to speak to the landlord. "We won't be using our bed tonight," said one man. "We'll have to be in the camp. The boss is expecting a flood."

"It's been raining hard in the hills," said the other. "It's certain to flood down here."

"Have you had supper?"

"Yes, sir. All the loggers have eaten. Only the boys from the sawmill are at the table now."

The two men left, and the landlord turned back to Captain Pike. "Well, their bad luck is your good luck. You and your boy may take their places. But you can't have the whole bed. A man from the sawmill is sleeping in it now."

"I'd like to bring our things in before it rains, but I hate to wake him."

"Nothing wakes Charlie. Put your things in the room. It's the first door on your left."

A few minutes later the travelers quietly entered their room.

"Father, look!" whispered Zeb. "That workman didn't undress. He didn't even take off his boots. Listen to him snore!"

"S-sh! We'll talk outside."

The Captain and Zeb put their saddlebags on the floor and left the room.

Then Zeb began, "Where are we going to sleep? That man is in the middle of the bed."

"We'll sleep on either side of him," said the Captain. "The poor fellow was too tired to undress. Lumbering is hard work, son."

"We can't get under the covers. That Charlie is lying on top of them."

"We have our bedrolls. We'll use our own covers. I'm just thankful we're not in a room with three beds—three men in each and all of them snoring!"

Zeb thought this was funny. He was still smiling when they went into the dining room.

"That's the first smile I've seen this evening," said a young workman. "It's like a ray of sunshine in the dark of night."

"He talks sort of fancy sometimes," said another workman. "He means that the loggers have been here and that all of them were bluer than indigo."

100

"Can you blame them?" asked another. "They get a pile of logs about ready to float down to the sawmill. Then along comes a flood and piles them every-which-way."

"The flood could cost the men three months' work," added another. "Just think—three months' work ruined by a wall of water!"

"A wall of water!" exclaimed Zeb.

"That's right, boy. I've seen it as high as this room. Men had to run from it."

"I suppose the loggers are moving the logs back from the stream," said the Captain.

"Yes, sir, they are using their teams. As soon as we get some rest, we'll help them."

ZEB'S ROOMMATE

Soon all the men had left but Jasper and Luke. They said they would keep Captain Pike and his son company while they ate supper.

"It's strange Charlie hasn't been in for supper," said Luke.

"He went to bed," said Jasper. "He said he was too tired to eat. But he asked me to call him if there was a flood. He wants to help."

"There's a man named Charlie in our room," said Zeb. "It's the first door on the left."

"He's the one, lad."

"I hope I won't keep him awake. My brother says I kick a lot some nights."

"A horse would have to kick Charlie to wake him," said Jasper.

"That's a fact," Luke agreed. "It will be Charlie keeping you awake, lad. He's the prize snorer of Bald Eagle Creek."

"I know a way to stop that," Jasper declared. "Just tie a string around his big toe and pull it every time he snores."

"But he had his boots on," said Zeb.

"He did? Well, he might get fighting mad

anyway," said Luke. "Getting someone to tie that string on Charlie's toe is like getting the mice to put a bell on the cat's neck. Who is going to tie the string? Not I!"

"Not I!" squeaked Jasper.

Zeb laughed and laughed, but finally his father said, "We'll have a hard ride tomorrow, son. It's time we went to bed."

The landlord was waiting with a candle. "You'd better not undress," he advised. "If there's a flood tonight, the water might get into the house. It has before, several times."

The travelers found their bedfellow still asleep, still snoring, and still in the middle of the bed. They got out their blankets and lay down on either side of him. They hadn't taken off their clothing or boots, either.

Captain Pike went to sleep, but Zeb couldn't. The snores sounded like thunder now. The boy tossed and turned. He sat up and lay down.

Suddenly Zeb remembered what Jasper had said. The boy didn't have a string, but he thought a grazing rope would do.

"The candle is still burning," he thought. "I should be able to find the rope."

In about two minutes Zeb was tying the rope over Charlie's boot at the ankle. Then he sat on a stool across the room. He tied knots in the rope to take up the slack. Now he wound the other end around his own ankle.

Now the fun began. Charlie snored, and Zeb jerked. Snore—jerk—snore—jerk—snore—jerk! This went on and on. The big workman was supposed to stop snoring, but he didn't.

Zeb didn't think the matter was fun any more. The candle had burned out, and the room was dark and cold. Zeb was tired and sleepy. He decided to untie the rope and go back to bed.

Instead, he went to sleep on the stool. He didn't hear the storm. He didn't know his father had left the room. A loud voice woke him up. "Wake up, Charlie! Wake up! There's a flood!"

Charlie woke up. "I'm coming!" he cried. "I'm coming!" He tried to get out of bed, but something held his foot.

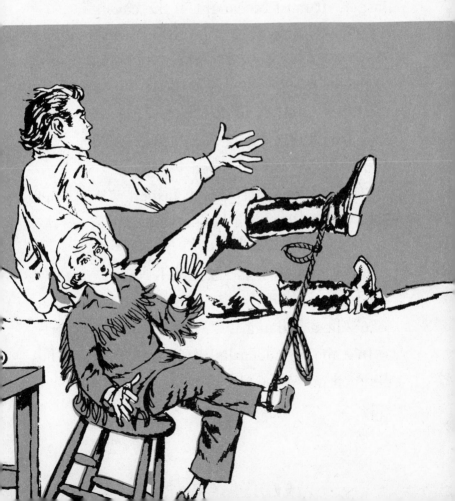

"You don't need to get up," said Jasper. "The other men have saved the logs. But I promised to wake you."

"I'll get up. It's daylight. It's about time to go to work. See what's the matter with my boot, Jasper. It must be caught in the covers."

"There's a leather rope around your ankle. Hey! What's this? The other end is tied to this boy over here."

"What boy?" Charlie sat up and jerked his roped foot. Poor Zeb was dragged off his stool and pulled toward the bed.

"Why, bless me!" cried Jasper. "If it isn't Zeb! Have you been belling the cat?"

"I tried, but——"

Jasper laughed and laughed.

Charlie scowled. "Is this some kind of a joke?" he asked angrily. "Cut this rope, Jasper!"

In a moment Charlie's foot was free, and he climbed out of bed.

"Shall I wait for you?" asked Jasper.

"No, go on. I've got a job to do here before I can leave."

Jasper left, and Charlie turned angrily to Zeb. "Now then, explain this!"

The boy knew the big man was fighting mad, and he was scared. He managed to explain, but all the time he wondered what Charlie would do to him. He was more than surprised when Charlie spoke. "So! I snore, do I?"

"Yes, sir."

"You couldn't stop me?"

"No, sir."

"You didn't go about it right, boy. You jerked my foot. Jasper said to jerk my big toe."

"Would that make a difference?"

"We'll find out tonight. You can try it again. I won't have my boots on."

"I won't be here tonight."

"You can't travel till the water goes down. The

trail will be covered. You'll be here all right. I'll get a good strong string for you."

"I was afraid you'd be angry with me."

"I was, but I'm not now. I like boys who go ahead and try things out. I'm proud to know you, Zeb."

But Zeb's father didn't agree with Charlie's idea. "You let other people's big toes alone," he said severely.

At the
Trading Post

ZEB DIDN'T SEE Charlie again. The flood waters had not come over the creek bank, and the trail was dry. Captain Pike and his son left the inn after an early breakfast.

Now they were in New York State and almost at the end of their journey. The Captain looked at his rough map. "MacFeeters' trading post should be near by," he said. "We should see it in a few minutes. Look for a stockade, Zeb."

"I see it!" the boy exclaimed a little later. "It does look like a fort."

"The trader and his furs will be safe from Indians behind that high stockade."

"The gate is wide open. He can't be afraid of them now, can he?"

"No—no—he can't. Zeb, remember, we must be very careful here. This trader must not suspect that I am a spy."

"He wouldn't warn the Indians, would he?"

"He would if he is selling them guns."

"Can't I help you watch him?"

"I'm afraid he'd catch you at it. I'll do the spying, Zeb."

There was no more talk. They had come to the opening in the stockade. Now they rode through into the large yard. At once the trader, William MacFeeters, came to meet them.

He said he was glad to have travelers stop. His family was away, so Captain Pike and his son would be company for him.

An Indian took their horses. Then Captain Pike explained his desire to go into the fur business. The trader seemed to believe him. "Several

110

soldiers have become trappers," he said. "You'll find their cabins around the lake. Some of them come here every day."

"Are Indian trappers bringing in skins?"

"Yes, it has been a good year for them."

"Is there any danger? I mean, do you think the Indians might go on the warpath?"

"No—and I would know if they were getting ready for war. They would want to trade their skins for knives and hatchets."

"And guns," the Captain added.

Mister MacFeeters gave him a sharp look. "They wouldn't try that with me," he declared. "They know I wouldn't sell a gun to any Indian. Now take any cabin that's empty and move in. I'll see you at supper."

Captain Pike chose a cabin next to the stockade gate. The minute he had closed the door Zeb exclaimed, "I know why you took this one! It will be easier to come and go."

"S-sh!" Captain Pike pointed to the wide cracks between logs. Then he spoke in a loud voice. "Yes, it will be easier to come and go. I want to visit all these soldier-trappers. I might know some of them."

Zeb took the hint. After that he whispered when he spoke about their secret.

COUNTING INDIAN TRAPPERS

Captain Pike left early the next morning. Zeb watched his father until he disappeared in the forest. Another boy was watching, too—an Indian boy about Zeb's age.

"Your father's gone now," said the boy with a friendly smile. "Your name's Zeb, isn't it? My name is Hawkeye."

"That used to be my name, too," said Zeb, also smiling. "All the boys on Bald Eagle Creek called me Hawkeye for a while."

"You can see far like a hawk?"

"Yes indeed."

"Can you see very far?"

"I can see farther than the other boys."

"I can see very far. No white boy can see as far as I can. I can hit a target far away."

"So can I," said Zeb, "and I can hit dead center almost every time."

"I do hit dead center every time," said the Indian boy.

A man laughed just behind them. He sat on a bench by the gate. "You two lads do like to brag, don't you?" he asked.

The boys laughed, and Hawkeye put his hand on the man's shoulder. "Zeb, this is Amos. He's a trapper. He likes to joke, but I don't care."

Now a squaw came from a cabin across the yard and called to Hawkeye. He went running.

"Hawkeye's a good boy," said the trapper. "He lives in that cabin with his parents. His mother is the cook here, and his father is the hunter for the post—and the fisherman, too."

"Will Hawkeye play with me?"

"He won't have much time to play right now. He hunts and fishes with his father. They are getting meat and fish to dry for the winter."

"Is he the only boy here?"

"Yes, but you won't have time to be lonely. I'll show you how to play a game that will keep you plenty busy."

"What kind of game?"

"You just sit here and count the Indian trappers when they come in with their skins. Then count them again when they leave."

"What for?"

The trapper laughed. "Your father said you would ask that."

"My father!" Zeb was surprised.

"Yes, I had a little talk with him this morning. We are old friends. We were soldiers together.

I told him about this game. You see, I've been playing it myself for several days."

"Do you want to know how many Indian trappers come here?"

"I want to know why only part of them leave. If six come, four leave. If three come, two leave. Always, some do not return from that store."

"Some of them might have stayed to work with the skins."

Amos shook his head. "No, they didn't stay. I looked in there each time."

"Is there another way out?"

"There's only one opening in the stockade—this gate."

"But the Indians have to get out someway. Perhaps you didn't count right."

"Perhaps I didn't—they came in bunches. That's why I want you to count them. You said you had eyes like a hawk."

Zeb laughed. "I'll count, sir."

Another trapper came along, and Amos left the post with him. "I'll be here tomorrow!" he called back to Zeb.

Zeb waited hours, but he didn't give up. It was almost noon when a group of Indian trappers came with skins. Zeb counted five men as they went into the store.

After a time three men came out and left by the gateway. Zeb hurried to the storeroom and looked in. There was only the trader's Indian helper there, and no one was loafing outside.

That afternoon Zeb saw four go in but just two come out. Later, one went in and none came out. Zeb waited for him till the supper bell rang.

That night Zeb was counting Indians in his sleep. He was hunting them, too. He was looking under beaver skins, bear skins, and even little rabbit skins. But he didn't find one trapper.

While Zeb was waiting for Amos the next morning, Hawkeye came to the gate. He car-

ried a fishing pole and net. But he didn't look happy, the way a boy ought to look when he's going fishing.

Zeb noticed this and wondered. He soon found out why. Hawkeye didn't like to fish.

"I love to fish!" exclaimed Zeb. "I wish I could go with you."

"I asked my father if you could and he said 'No,'" the Indian boy replied.

"Why?" asked Zeb.

"Father said I must not play. I must fish all the time. I must catch many fish and get them ready to dry. I must chop off their heads and tails. Chop, chop, chop! I don't like that. The stone hurts my hand."

"Stone! Don't you use a knife?"

"I don't have one. The trader won't give me one, either."

"Take mine. I won't need it." Zeb took the sheath from his belt and gave it to Hawkeye.

The Indian boy was delighted. He drew the long hunting knife from the sheath. He ran a finger carefully along the sharp edge. He started away, but came back at once. He patted Zeb's arm fondly. Then he ran toward his cabin.

Presently Amos came, and Zeb told him about the Indians he had counted.

"Then I didn't make a mistake?"

"No, sir. I've been thinking—could there be a tunnel under the store?"

"There could be. There's a large cellar."

"The tunnel would come out in the woods. I'm going to look for the opening."

"A friend of mine tried that. He didn't come back. He was found the next day with an arrow in his heart."

"Someone didn't want him to find the tunnel."

"Or maybe he did find it, and the Indians were afraid he'd tell. I think there's some kind of a secret in the cellar."

Zeb was really excited now. "I can find out," he said quickly. "I can slip down there while the trader is eating."

"Stay out of that cellar, Zeb! You'd be caught."

"S-sh!" Zeb warned. "The trader is coming. He's behind you."

"Pretend I'm telling you a story and laugh. Quick!"

"Ha, ha, ha!" laughed Zeb. "That's a funny story, sir. Is it true?"

"I can't say as to that."

Mr. MacFeeters stopped. "What's so funny?" he asked.

"Oh, I just told one of my bear stories. You've heard them all."

"I see. Could you look at some skins, Amos? I'd like your opinion of them."

Amos was busy in the post store all morning. Zeb saw him at dinner, but the trader talked to him all the time about furs.

Only once did Mr. MacFeeters speak to Zeb. "I've noticed you at the gate. Were you waiting for your father?"

"I—I thought he might come."

"The boy is lonely," said Amos.

"It won't do to watch all the time. Stay away from the gate, Zeb. Find something else to do."

After dinner Zeb went to his cabin. The trader had given him a hint about the gate. Did the man know he had been counting Indians? He was worried and scared. He wished his father was here. He wished he was home with Mother and Jimmie and Maria.

THE SECRET OF THE CELLAR

Zeb was delighted to see Hawkeye a little later. He had brought the knife back. But Zeb didn't care much about that. He just wanted company, so he asked the boy to come in.

"Your knife is a good one," said Hawkeye. "I chopped fast with it. I would like to have it. Would you trade?"

"Trade for what?" asked Zeb.

"I know a secret. I'll tell it to you for the knife. What do you say?"

"What kind of secret, Hawkeye?"

The Indian boy went to the door and looked out. Then he crossed to Zeb and whispered one word in his ear—"Tunnel."

Zeb was so excited his heart almost stopped. But he didn't let Hawkeye know it. "Where is it?" he asked.

"It runs under the store out to the woods. I'll show it to you now."

"Where is the trader?"

"He's gone to the Indian camp. Everyone has gone to see the braves dance. This is a good time to show you the tunnel. Are you coming?"

Zeb hadn't forgotten what Amos had said, but

things were different now. No one could catch him. Everyone was away.

"How can we get into the store, Hawkeye? The door will be locked."

"We can get in through a window—I know."

Zeb followed Hawkeye to the store, then through it to the cellar door and steps. The boys crept down quietly. The light from the open door above showed a large half-dark room.

Zeb looked about quickly. He saw several long chests. "Are the chests for furs?" he asked.

"Maybe. I never looked. Come!" Hawkeye ran to a side wall and tried to open a small door.

Zeb didn't follow. His sharp eyes had seen a chest with the lid raised. He went to it and looked in. It was full of guns!

Everything was plain now. The trader was the gun seller! The Indian trappers who stayed carried guns out through the tunnel.

All this flashed through Zeb's mind in an instant. He crossed the room quickly. Hawkeye was still tugging at the door. Now it opened, and Zeb saw a long dark passage.

"Here's the tunnel," said Hawkeye.

Zeb reached for his sheath. At this very moment the boys heard steps on the floor above.

"It's the trader," whispered Hawkeye. "Come! Into the tunnel! Quick!"

The Indian boy closed the door softly behind them—and just in time. The footsteps sounded on the cellar stairs.

The boys raced through the dark passage. Any minute that door might open. Now they saw sunlight. In another minute they were out of the tunnel and in the woods. The stockade was behind them.

Zeb stopped to unfasten his knife sheath from his belt, but Hawkeye seized his arm. "Don't stop! Get to your cabin in the post quickly. Don't let the trader see you. Run!"

End of an Adventure

THE BOYS reached the stockade gate just as the supper bell began to ring.

"I can't eat with Mr. MacFeeters," said Zeb. "I'd be afraid."

"I'll take care of that. Stay in your cabin. I'll bring your supper to you and get my knife then," said Hawkeye.

Zeb closed his door quickly. There was neither bar nor latchstring, but the boy felt safer inside than he had a few minutes before. He began to feel braver, too, as he waited for his young Indian friend.

"Maybe the trader didn't hear the tunnel door

close," thought Zeb. "Maybe he didn't see us. I don't need to worry about him."

But Zeb was worried about his supper. He wondered why Hawkeye hadn't brought it and come for his knife. Suddenly Zeb thought of something that scared him again.

"Hawkeye must have told his parents about the knife. He probably told them that he showed me the tunnel, too. Now they won't let him come. They'll come themselves. They'll try to take me away so I can't tell the secret.

"But they won't get me! I'll run away! I'll find Amos!"

Zeb began to roll his blankets and clothing. Then he stopped. "I can't find Amos at night. I don't even know where his cabin is." The boy didn't know what to do.

"What will these Indians do with me?" he asked himself. "Where will they take me? Will I ever see my family again?"

126

Now there was a noise at the door. Zeb seized his gun and waited. The door opened, and Captain Pike came in.

Zeb was so astonished he couldn't say anything. He dropped his gun—he just stood there and stared.

"Zeb! What's the matter? Are you ill?"

"I was scared. I thought——"

"S-sh! Speak softly!"

"I've got something to tell you."

"We can't talk now. We must get away from here at once. Get your things, and hurry! I'll roll your blankets and clothes."

The Captain led the way from the cabin and through the gateway. Then Zeb had another surprise. Amos was waiting outside with their horses and his own. They mounted silently and rode away into the moonlit night.

After some time they stopped to rest. "I've got something to tell you," Zeb began.

"S-sh!" whispered both men.

"We think Indians are following us," said Captain Pike softly.

At daybreak the riders dismounted. "There's a cave here," said Amos. "We could hide in it today. What do you say, Captain?"

"You're in charge. You know this north country better than I do."

"Maybe, but we both know Indians pretty well, so there'll be no fire to cook our breakfast. The redskins might see the smoke."

"I have something to tell you," Zeb began.

"We'll eat first," said the guide. "I have food in my pack. We'll eat in this cave."

Amos pulled back a mass of vines from the cliff to reveal a small opening. Then he looked inside carefully. "There is no redskin in there— and no animal either," he said.

The men took care of the horses, and Zeb carried their packs into the cave.

Soon the men entered the cave, and Amos opened his food bags. "May I talk now?" asked Zeb. "I have something to tell you."

"No," said Amos. "Eat now. We'll talk afterward. The savages might come. We don't want to leave here hungry."

Presently the spies were enjoying their breakfast. The dried meat and parched corn tasted good to all of them. Soon they had finished, and Amos spoke. "Go ahead, Zeb. What's that you've been trying to tell us?"

"Keep your voice down," said Captain Pike, "and don't get excited."

WHAT HAPPENED TO THE TRADER

But it was the men who became excited, as they listened to Zeb's story. He told about his trade with Hawkeye and how he saw the guns and ran through the secret tunnel.

130

"Well! Well!" exclaimed his father.

"By cracky!" cried Amos.

"Hawkeye and I ran fast," Zeb added. "We thought the trader was after us. We heard him start down the cellar steps."

"What made you think it was Mr. MacFeeters?" asked his father.

"It was someone with boots."

"It was my boots you heard, Zeb."

"Yours! You! Were you——?"

"S-sh!" warned Amos.

Captain Pike went on. "I went down into the cellar. I saw the guns and the tunnel. I had got into the store through an open window."

"We thought we'd get out that way."

"That's what I thought, but I didn't. I met the trader as I came up out of the cellar. He had just come in."

Zeb was excited now. "My goodness! What did he say to you?"

"Nothing, but was he angry! He raised his gun—he meant to shoot me. He would have shot me, too, if Amos hadn't seized him from behind. We tied him up and left him in the store."

"His Indian helpers will set him free," Amos added. "He can't escape if they do."

"The Colonel will send soldiers to seize him and take him to the fort in Carlisle," Captain Pike explained.

"Well, Zeb," said Amos, "we know the answer to our game now."

"Yes, sir. Each time Indians went into the store, some stayed to carry out guns for themselves and the others."

"The trader thought he'd fool us old trappers, but he was wrong. We knew all along that those braves weren't real trappers. They were gunrunners from the Indian camp. We hid on the hill and watched them. We saw the same men leave with bundles of guns."

132

"I'll give you and your friends credit for this information," said Captain Pike. "The Colonel shall know all about it."

"We don't want credit. Americans ought to help one another."

"The trader didn't," said Zeb.

"I think he went crazy over money."

"I agree with you," said Captain Pike. "He couldn't be in his right mind."

"Well, Zeb," said Amos, "I haven't had a chance to scold you yet for going into that cellar. I told you to stay out of there."

"He should be scolded," said Captain Pike.

"But I found where the tunnel came out in the woods!"

"By cracky, you did!" exclaimed Amos. "You're ahead of your father there. I'm afraid he'll have a hard time when he sees the Colonel. How can he make anyone believe that he's as good a spy as you are?"

"Ha, ha!" laughed the spies. But they laughed very softly.

Then two slept while one stood guard. That one was never young Zeb. The men saw to this.

HOME AGAIN

At last it was all over, and Zeb was at home. His father and Amos had gone on to Carlisle after resting a few days. Zeb was doing the outside work and glad he could be there to do it. It was nice to work and not be scared.

It was nice to be in the pretty, clean cabin with Mother and the children. He felt safe and happy. "I'll never go away again," he said. "I love it here."

He told the twins this, and they just couldn't understand.

"If I could travel, I wouldn't mind being scared," said one.

"Neither would I," said the other. "I wouldn't care if I was scared to death."

"That's big talk," said Zeb. "You'd have been scared as much as I was."

The twins denied this of course. They said they didn't scare easily.

"I don't scare easily either."

"Lucy said you did."

"Lucy! Do you know her?"

The boys said that Lucy and her family had lived in that old cabin near their pasture for a while. Then they went back to Trenton.

"Lucy said you were afraid of her," said Dan.

"I was not! I just didn't want to talk with her," said Zeb.

"She told us we were pretty," said Dave.

"You! Pretty?"

The twins nodded and grinned.

"I can't understand that. Lucy told me I was pretty, too—and we don't look alike."

The twins shook their heads. They also were puzzled.

"I'm glad she's gone," Zeb declared, "and I hope she never comes back."

The twins said they hoped so, too. But not one of the three meant it, and each one knew the others didn't.

The next time Zeb saw his friends, Lucy was forgotten. He had come to tell them good-by. They were moving to a new settlement far away, on the Ohio River.

The twins bragged about the sights they would see—the great mountains and wide rivers.

"We'll float down the Ohio River in a big flat-boat," said Dan. "Indians will watch us float by, and I'll wave to them. Ha, ha!"

"They'll be hopping mad because they can't shoot us," said Dave. "Ha, ha!"

"Why can't they?" Zeb asked.

"We'll be out in the middle of the river."

"Their arrows can't reach us," put in Dan.

"I'd like to float down a river," said Zeb. "I wish my folks would move."

Zeb told his mother all this as soon as he got home. "Just think, Mother, we wouldn't bounce the way we do in a wagon. We'd just sit on the boat deck and float and float and float."

"Yes, and the Indians on the shore would just shoot and shoot and shoot."

"Their arrows wouldn't hit us. We'd be out in midstream."

"No, Zeb, we're not going to move anywhere. We've moved enough—and you've traveled enough. We'll stay right here on Bald Eagle Creek. I hope we'll never have to leave."

By Wagon and Flatboat

THE SPRING after Zeb's fourteenth birthday, 1793, the Pikes were moving again. They were traveling in a large covered wagon, and they were bound for the Ohio River country.

They weren't moving to a new settlement as the Ryans had. They were to live in a fort.

"I never thought I would be cooking over a fire by the roadside again," Mrs. Pike said the first day at noon. "But here I am, frying bacon and corncakes.

"I thought we were settled on Bald Eagle Creek for life. Now our farm has been sold, and we're moving to goodness-knows-what."

138

"You can blame the Indians for that," said Captain Pike. "More officers and men had to be sent to frontier forts to protect settlers. I thought it was my duty to join the army again and help."

"It was your duty, Zebulon. I'm proud of the work they gave you. It is an honor to be the commander of Fort Washington."

"Are there many soldiers there now, Father?" asked Zeb.

"There are fewer than two hundred. But more will be sent. I hope Amos will be one of the officers."

"I hope he'll come," said Zeb. "I have fun with him."

"I hope the Ryans live near the fort," said Mrs. Pike.

"I'll find out as soon as we arrive."

"Can Dave and Dan come to the fort to see us?" asked Zeb.

"Of course," said the Captain.

"I'm tired," said Jimmie.

"I'm tired, too," said four-year-old Maria.

"I'll make up the feather bed, and you can both take naps," said Mother. "But you must not talk—you might wake baby George."

"Jimmie and Maria will never know when the horses are hitched," said Zeb. "They'll be asleep in five minutes."

"Get ready to go," said the Captain. "Put out the fire—crush every tiny spark."

Then the travelers began to move again, on and on toward the west. They crossed beautiful green valleys and shining rivers. Zeb and his father walked to lighten the load.

Jimmie usually wanted to walk with them, but he couldn't climb a hill. He was nine years old now, but he was still weak. Mrs. Pike always said she wanted him to help her drive. She said she and Maria were afraid to ride alone.

140

This pleased Jimmie, and he would sit beside her. But Mrs. Pike refused to drive over the first great mountain.

"I'm afraid I can't keep the wheels on the road," she said. "I'm afraid the wagon will fall over the cliff."

"This is a narrow steep road," said Captain Pike. "I'll drive."

Mrs. Pike climbed on foot with Zeb. At noon the Captain stopped at the side of a mountain brook. The clear, cold water came tumbling down over the cliff. The travelers ate lunch there so they could drink the water.

"It's pretty here," said Zeb. "I think I could stay here forever."

"Forever is a long time," said Father. "I'm afraid I can't wait for you."

At last the Pikes were over the mountains. Soon they reached a settlement on the bank of the great Ohio River.

"This is Pittsburgh," said the Captain.

"That's a big name for such a little place," said Zeb. "There are only a few log cabins."

"Most of the flatboats start from here. Ours does. It's probably waiting for us now. The Colonel ordered it some time ago."

Captain Pike started down the steep bank. "Hold tight, everybody! I don't want anyone to fall out of the wagon!"

"ALL ABOARD!"

At first the travelers couldn't see the river bank because of a great growth of trees. Now they had a good view.

"My goodness!" exclaimed Zeb. "Look at all the people!"

"Look at the wagons!" cried Jimmie.

"Are all of those people waiting for flatboats?" asked Mrs. Pike.

"They must be. The men aren't wearing uniforms. They are probably settlers moving to new settlements on the river.

By this time the Captain had found a place along the shore for his wagon. At once people hurried up to speak to him.

"We want to go downriver," a man explained. "A crowd arrived here just ahead of us and took all the flatboats except one."

"The one that is left is for some officer," said another man.

"That's not right!" a woman cried. "First come, first served, I say!"

"Of course it isn't right!" agreed another woman. "Here we have to wait until new flatboats can be built."

"I'm glad you do," Captain Pike said gravely. "I hope you'll have to wait till more soldiers come and new forts can be built along the river. There is great danger from Indians now."

143

"I don't need any fort for my family to run to," declared a frontiersman. "I can shoot better than any Indian."

"That's the way I feel," said another.

Others nodded. Then a woman spoke. "I've always said that Indians would be kind to us if we were kind to them."

"Don't count on kindness now," replied the Captain. "Several different tribes have decided to drive white people from the Ohio River country. If they unite, there won't be a settlement left along the river, unless the President sends an army out here."

"Then why are you going?" asked a man.

"I'm going to protect you if you settle near Fort Washington. I'm going to repair the fort and make it large enough to hold all of you if the Indians attack."

"Then you must be the new commander of the fort," said a man.

144

The crew of the flatboat had seen the new-comers arrive, so now the crewmaster came up. "Are you Captain Pike, sir?"

"I am."

"Your boat is ready, sir. Mr. Jones here will buy your wagon."

"I build flatboats from wagon lumber," Mr. Jones explained. "I'll buy your horses also, Captain. You won't need them. There are horses at Fort Washington already."

While the sale was being made, Zeb was carrying bundles from the wagon to the flatboat. Mrs. Pike and Jimmie were helping. Captain Pike was helping, too, before the work was done.

Now the wagon was empty, and the Pikes went aboard. The polers pushed the boat from the shore with long poles. The crewmaster steered it out to midstream. The people on the shore waved, and the Pikes waved back.

"Those settlers won't wait for forts and

soldiers," said Captain Pike. "They are in a hurry to take the rich land along the river."

"Each man will try to get ahead of the others," said Mrs. Pike, "even if he's in danger of losing his scalp to the Indians."

FLAMING ARROWS

The boys had been on the forward deck ever since they went aboard. Jimmie sat now on a pile of dry tow. Zeb sat on a coil of heavy rope. King was asleep near by. The boys couldn't take their eyes from the sparkling water and the green hills on each side of the river.

"What a pretty sight!" exclaimed Zeb. "It seems as though we are floating into fairyland— with the blue water, white sand, and blue mist over the hilltops."

"Have you ever seen the fairies, Mister?" Jimmie asked the poler.

146

"I haven't had time to look for them. I've been too busy watching for Indians."

"Do you think we'll see Indians?" asked Zeb.

"Yes, I'm afraid we will. They are nearly always on a big island just around the next bend in the river. You'll see it in a little while, boys. Keep your eyes open."

The boys waited. Then Zeb cried, "I see it! It's closer to the shore on the right side."

"We have to pass on that side," said the poler. "The current runs there."

"That will bring us close to the Indians, won't it?" asked Jimmie.

"It will bring us too close to suit me. I've seen the Indians' painted faces. But you'll be safe in the cabin. You're to go there now. The crewmaster told me to tell you."

When the boys went in, they saw Mother cooking over the small fire in the fireplace. Father was placing benches at a small table.

"Get ready for supper, boys," said Mrs. Pike. "Wash your hands. Here's a bucket of water."

Just at that moment the crewmaster entered. "We're about to pass that island," he said. "We can see Indians there. You're to stay in here till I say the danger is over. Arrows will be flying in a few minutes."

"You certainly won't stay out on deck with your men!" exclaimed Mrs. Pike.

"No, Ma'am. The current will carry the boat along. We'll be in here shooting from these loopholes in the walls."

"I'll be shooting with you," said Captain Pike.

"I will, too," said Zeb. "I have my own gun."

"I'm sorry, lad, but boys aren't allowed to use firearms aboard. I'll be glad to have your help, though, Captain."

Now the polers rushed in. "The island is alive with Indians!" one man cried. "They're on the shore and in the trees!"

148

"Their faces are painted!" cried another.

"I'd like to see them," said Zeb. "May I open the door just a crack, Master?"

"No! You might let an arrow fly in!"

"See that Maria and Jimmie don't open the door either," added Captain Pike.

"The baby is asleep, but you must watch him, too," said Mrs. Pike.

Each man placed the muzzle of his gun in a loophole and waited for the master's voice.

Now came the *ping-ping* of arrows striking the wooden walls of the cabin.

"Fire!" shouted the master.

Zeb wanted to do something to help. It wasn't enough just to take care of the younger children. "Mother is reloading guns," he thought. "May I help you, Mother?" he asked out loud.

"I don't need you just now. Stay by the door and watch it as your father told you."

Zeb listened at the door, his ear against a

crack. He heard the Indians' shouting, yelling, and screaming. Then he heard another sound right at the door. It was the whining and crying of a dog. It was King!

Zeb had forgotten him during the excitement about the Indians. The master would be angry if Zeb opened the door. But if he didn't, King might be killed by a flying arrow.

The boy couldn't leave the poor dog out there. He wouldn't! He opened the door, and King rushed in. It didn't take a minute, but in that minute Zeb saw a terrible sight.

A flaming arrow was falling into the dry tow where Jimmie had been sitting. A flame shot up at once, and the Indians yelled with joy.

Zeb knew the fire would spread quickly. The deck was made from old wagon lumber and was very dry. The flames would reach the cabin.

That fire had to be put out. The next instant Zeb had the water bucket and was running along the deck. Arrows were striking somewhere, but he reached the flaming tow.

He threw the water on it, and the flame died out. He started back, running. The Indians were shouting angrily. The boy knew they'd kill him if they could, so he ran bent over low and dodging from side to side.

But somehow the *ping-ping* sounded farther away. Not an arrow fell close to Zeb as he raced to the cabin door.

The master had just ordered the men to stop shooting. "We've passed the island!" he called. "We're out of danger!"

The men were leaving the loopholes when Zeb came in with his bucket.

"What's this?" asked the astonished master.

"Zeb!" cried the astonished parents

"I've been putting out a fire." Then he explained about the dog and the flaming arrow.

"That was a brave deed," said the master. "It

happened just as we had passed the island. Their arrows couldn't quite reach you."

"You saved the boat, lad!" cried a poler.

"You saved our lives," said his father.

"I'm proud of you," said his mother.

"What a riverman the boy would make!" exclaimed the master.

"Aye! Aye! He would!" cried the polers.

Fort Washington

DURING THE NEXT two weeks the boat passed several small islands, but no Indians were seen. Then late one night the boat reached another large island. The rivermen didn't tie up as they usually did at dark.

"The moon's shining brightly," said the master. "We'll float by. I'm glad the passengers are asleep. They won't be scared this way."

"I never knew the Indians to attack at night," said a poler.

"They'll be here by dawn," said another man. "There will be fifty canoes on the shore."

The boat had floated halfway around the

island when it suddenly stopped. It was aground on a sand bar! The crew tried to push it off, but couldn't budge it. Finally the master woke Captain Pike and asked him to help. "If we don't get off this bar soon, the redskins will be coming aboard," he said.

In five minutes the Captain was dressed and poling with the others. In two more minutes a new hand was helping—and he wasn't sent back to bed either.

"Look at the boy push," a poler said softly. "He's as strong as an ox."

"He is that!" said another. "He knows how to use his pole, too."

Finally the boat was off the sand bar. But it was almost dawn before it had passed the island.

"We made it," said the master, "but it was by the skin of our teeth. We couldn't have done it without your help, Captain—and yours, Zeb."

The master patted the boy on the back. "You'd

155

make a first-class poler, lad. How did you get such strong muscles, anyway?"

"I've been chopping down trees, sir."

"I could use you, Zeb, when you're fifteen years old or so."

"I'd like to be a riverman," said the boy. "Then I could travel all the time."

Then there were more days of floating on the smooth water under a bright blue sky. Then came the end. One morning the master told his passengers to get ready to go ashore.

"This is the last bend. As soon as we round it, you'll see the fort and the settlement."

A little later Zeb cried, "I see the fort! I see the fort! It's on that high bank, Jimmie. There's a stockade around it."

"Look at the people gathered on the river-bank!" exclaimed Mrs. Pike.

"They've come to welcome you and your family," said the crewmaster.

Now the flatboat landed, and the passengers went ashore. Almost at once they were surrounded by people from the settlement.

"We're glad you've come, Captain," said a carpenter. "We need a man like you at the fort."

"We know you're an old Indian fighter," said a gunsmith. "You'll know how to protect our settlement."

Now the lieutenant from the fort led the newcomers up the steep bank. The people waved and shouted words of welcome.

The garrison stood at attention just inside the stockade gate.

"At ease!" ordered Captain Pike. "I don't know what this small force could do if a thousand warriors attack, Lieutenant."

"We have six cannon, sir."

"Good! We can at least make noise. Maybe we can scare the Indians away."

"I hope you're right, sir."

The Captain and his family lived in a cabin inside the fort. It had one room and a loft where the two boys slept. It was just like the cabins where the other officers lived.

After everything was in place Mrs. Pike was pleased. "Before long we'll think this cabin is as cozy as the one on Bald Eagle Creek—and we'll like living here."

"I won't," said Zeb. "There aren't any boys my age here. Either they're young like Jimmie, or else they're babies."

The following day Zeb had another disappointment. The Ryan family wasn't in the settlement. "No one has seen them," said the Captain.

"Where are they, Father?"

"I don't know, but you couldn't visit them if they were here, unless a soldier went with you. From now on, no one will be allowed to leave this fort without a guard."

"Has something happened?" asked Mrs. Pike.

"Yes. A hunter has just told me that he saw an Indian hiding among bushes in the forest this morning," said the Captain.

"Did the Indian know the hunter saw him?" asked Zeb.

"No, the hunter pretended he hadn't. He said that the Indian was so quiet the bushes didn't even move. The redskin no doubt was a scout. Indians always send out scouts before an attack."

"Are you expecting an attack on the fort?"

"Yes—and at any time."

The Captain kept his men busy with drills and target practice. Zeb watched every chance he had, but he was nearly always busy himself with work for the fort.

He had to keep all the cook fires going. He had to cut logs to fit fireplaces. But he was guarded by a soldier every time he worked outside.

He had a guard when he went to the hillside to pick blackberries and when he went fishing and swimming. But he wasn't allowed to hunt. Hunting was done by a party of soldiers with other soldiers to guard them.

It was the same way in the settlement. If a woman went out for greens, a man guarded her. If children went to the river to wade, fathers with guns stayed close by.

Parents knew it would be easy for an Indian to slip up in a canoe, seize a child, and carry him away. Children had been stolen from other settlements in this way.

Men were afraid to make gardens or go to their fields alone, so they took turns guarding one another. Of course there was always a guard at the fort gate which was opened only when it was necessary.

The settlers kept asking Captain Pike when the new soldiers would come. They said they might be able to get to the fort after they were warned. But could only a few soldiers hold it against hundreds of Indians?

Zeb knew his father was worried and decided to help him. "Father, why couldn't I join the army now?" he asked. "I'd make one more soldier for you. I'm fourteen years old."

"You'll have to wait till you're fifteen."

"But, Father——"

"Zeb, your father said fifteen," said Mrs. Pike sharply. "You are not to argue the matter."

This was Zeb's third disappointment. But maybe Father would change his mind if those soldiers didn't come soon.

MOCCASIN PRINTS

One evening at dusk two large flatboats landed with ammunition and other supplies for the fort. But there were no new soldiers.

Zeb was allowed to go with a squad of soldiers who were to unload. But he was only to watch.

"You must not try to help," his father said. "You'd get in the way."

It was fun at first to count the bundles, bags, and chests. But by the time the wagon was half full Zeb was tired of counting. He walked along the shore looking for shells for his mother. She liked the pretty pink ones.

He would pick up one and examine it. Then he would either throw it away or put it in his pocket. Suddenly he saw a footprint in the wet sand. It was the print of an Indian moccasin! Close by were many other moccasin prints.

Zeb knew the tracks were fresh. "They were made this morning," he thought. "Indians have just come in canoes. They've hidden them in these willows, and they are hiding there themselves. They are watching me now."

The boy was frightened, but he didn't lose his

162

head. He used it and did something very smart. He acted as if he hadn't noticed the footprints. He went right on picking up shells and looking at them, then throwing them away or putting them in his pocket.

Now he came to more prints, many more. "Other canoes have just landed here," he thought. Then he knew the truth. They had come to attack the fort and settlement! They were waiting for more canoes with more warriors!

Zeb knew he had to get back—he had to tell his father. But he didn't dare to run. The Indians might think he had seen them. So he stopped and threw rocks far out into the river—just to see how far he could throw.

All the time his heart was pounding and his knees were weak. Once he glanced at the willows. He was sure he saw brown eagle feathers among the green branches. Then he started back toward the landing, but he didn't hurry.

Now a soldier called him. "Zeb! Come along! We've finished loading!"

Then Zeb ran like a deer. He told the soldiers what he had seen and how he pretended.

"We'll pretend, too," said the sergeant. "We'll talk and laugh till we get to the top of the bank. Then you men hurry to the fort and warn the Captain. I'll warn the settlers."

"I'll do that," said Zeb. "The Indians will think I belong there." He was gone before anyone could stop him.

There were only a few cabins. It didn't take long to knock at doors softly and whisper the alarm. "Run to the fort! Indians! They're hiding under the bank!"

At once the people started with their children, bedding, and food. They kept away from the riverbank so Indians hiding below it couldn't see them.

At the last cabin a woman told Zeb about new-

comers. "They just landed here yesterday," she said. "They're in that old cabin down the road a little way."

It was a long way, Zeb thought, but he went on. He was afraid the Indians would attack and cut off the strangers from the fort. These people had to be warned, though. At last he reached the cabin and knocked on the door.

It was opened, and there stood the Ryan boys —the twins—Dan and Dave! "Zeb!" they shouted. "Ma! Pa! Here's Zeb!"

"S-sh!" Zeb warned. "We'll talk later. Run to the fort! Quick! Indians! Don't stop to get anything! Follow me!"

He went running. When he reached the fort, the Ryans were close behind. The guard opened the gate, and now they were all inside.

Then savage yells were heard. Warriors came running from the shore. They surrounded the fort. They tried to break down the gate.

Arrows were flying. Bullets were whining, and then came the boom of the six cannon. That settled it. The Indians couldn't fight the iron monsters. They ran back to the river. It was all over in a few minutes.

Zeb found the Ryan twins. "Now then, let's talk," he said.

"What about?" asked Dan.

"Lucy," said Zeb.

The twins nearly died laughing. That was the funniest thing they had ever heard. Zeb thought it was funny himself, so he laughed with them.

Indians were forgotten. The friends were together again and having fun.

On the Upper Mississippi

IN AUGUST, 1805, a large flatboat lay at the Mississippi River landing below an Indian village. Twenty armed soldiers waited on the deck for their commanding officer. A fur trader was with them.

Now Lieutenant Zebulon Montgomery Pike came from the cabin. He wore the handsome uniform of an infantry officer of the United States Army. He was a fine-looking young man, and all his men were proud of his appearance.

His coat was trimmed with gold braid and brass buttons. Its high collar touched his chin. His white cloth trousers were spotless. His leather boots were gleaming. A handsome sword hung from the officer's belt.

"Is the Indian chief ready to meet with me?" he asked the trader.

"The Chief is waiting in his council house with his warriors, sir."

"Are you sure you can translate my words?"

"Yes, Lieutenant, I am sure I can. But I'm not so sure about this council. The Sac Indians are hostile to Americans."

"Why? We have never harmed them."

"But they fear you will. They know the United States has bought this country up here from France."

"Yes, the Louisiana Purchase, as it is called, is an immense country. It extends from the Mississippi River west to the mountains and from Canada to Mexico.

"The Sacs fear they will be driven from their lands. Their chief told me so this morning."

169

"I'll tell the Chief that the United States wants to be at peace with his people and that I was sent to offer President Jefferson's friendship to the Sacs."

"I fear he won't believe you. I know his warriors won't. They have been turned against your country by certain fur traders, who have told terrible lies about Americans."

"Do you know who these men were?"

"They were British fur traders. You see, they have been pushing down from Canada since the French left. They have trading posts down to the Missouri River. They are getting rich, and they don't want American traders coming here."

"So they want the Indians to drive out all Americans! Maybe even kill us!"

"I fear for your life, Lieutenant, if you go to this Sac village now."

"I have been ordered to visit every tribe, from here to the north border of our new territory. I have never yet run away from my duty. Come, we will go ashore."

Ten soldiers followed, while the others remained to guard the boat.

"That took courage," said one of those left with the boat. "Lieutenant Pike is a brave man."

"He's been fighting Indians ever since he joined the army at the age of fifteen," said the crewmaster of the flatboat.

"He had charge of a line of army flatboats when he was only seventeen years old," said a soldier. "He carried supplies to the forts on the Ohio River, and he had to dodge Indian arrows or bullets on every trip."

"Here lately he's been in charge of an army post at Kaskaskia in the Illinois country," said the crewmaster. "I'd say that Lieutenant Pike knows more about frontier life than any other officer in the army."

"That's why he was chosen to lead this expedition. This Louisiana Purchase is wild country. We'll need a leader who can take care of himself and us out here."

"The Lieutenant deserves good luck. I hope he's smoking the peace pipe right now."

"It's too soon for that," said a sergeant. "There'll be long speeches first."

"He's coming now!" cried the lookout. "I see his blue coat through the trees!"

"There's been trouble!" the master shouted. "Man the cannon! Hold your guns ready to fire! The Indians may pursue them."

But Lieutenant Pike and his men reached the boat safely. At once it was pushed off and steered to midstream.

Then he explained. "The Sacs wouldn't accept our flag. They made threatening motions with tomahawks. I told them President Jefferson would send a large army against them if one of us were hurt."

172

"It was your courage and bold words that saved us," the interpreter declared. "I fear you'll have the same trouble with all of these tribes."

"Well, the Indians can't prevent me from making maps of this country, nor from choosing places for American forts."

"No they can't—unless they capture you," said the interpreter to himself.

ENEMY TRADERS AND BITTER COLD

On up the Mississippi they went. Time and again the crew saw their leader go ashore to meet with Indian chiefs. Every time they feared he wouldn't return, but he always did.

Every night Lieutenant Pike wrote reports of what he had seen. He described the land, plants, and animals. He described the different tribes. He gave the number of warriors in each one. He made a map of every section he visited.

173

"We may have to fight these tribes some day," he told the interpreter. "These maps will show our army where to make camp and attack."

Only one chief had accepted the American flag. He was a Sioux. He declared he wanted peace with his great new white father, President Jefferson.

"Wait till the British hear this," said the interpreter. "They'll buy him back with gifts."

"The British traders are our worst enemies," said Pike. "I'm finding that out every time I stop at one of their trading posts. They seem to think England still owns America."

"I feared they would insult you."

"They have, many times. But I am obliged to give them a message from our government. They have built forts and trading posts on American land. They did not ask permission, and they have never paid a cent of rent. They laugh in my face when I remind them."

174

"I suppose it sounds funny to them—that an American would dare to demand anything from Englishmen."

"We may have to fight another war before they get the idea. We'll reach one of their trading posts tomorrow. Come with me. You shall hear what this British trader says."

The interpreter went. This is what he heard.

"Sir, you are conducting your business on American soil," said Lieutenant Pike. "You must pay rent to the United States."

The trader was indignant. "Since when can you tell an Englishman what to do?" he asked.

"Since General Washington fought a war with England and won it," replied the Lieutenant. "Have you ever heard about that? You may send your rent to the Congress of the United States. Thank you and good day, sir."

The interpreter and the lieutenant laughed about this for a long, long time.

Soon came new and worse trouble. The river had become so rough that the men couldn't manage the big heavy boat. They had to leave it and use small dugouts. Then the river froze, and the men couldn't use even the dugouts.

The men walked and dragged their supplies on sleds. Many became ill. Nearly all of them suffered from frozen hands and feet. At last they could go no farther. They halted and began to build a stockade for a winter camp. This would shut out wild animals as well as the fierce Chippewa Indians.

One night the Lieutenant's tent caught fire. He got out just in time. But much of his warm clothing was burned.

Had the Chippawa done this? Had their flaming arrows started the fire? The sentry claimed he had seen no one.

Pike was the strongest man in the company. He built sleds. He was a wonderful marksman.

176

He hunted for game and then cooked it. He nursed sick men back to health. Every night he wrote his report and drew maps.

When the sick men had recovered, the Lieutenant announced that he was going on.

"My orders said to explore up to the northern border of the Louisiana Purchase. We haven't reached that border yet, men."

The men said it would be too dangerous to travel now. The snow was too deep. Their commander would get lost. There was danger from wild animals, as well as danger from Chippewas.

"I must take those risks," the Lieutenant said. "Our new territory extends to the source of the Mississippi River. I must locate that source and make a map of the territory."

Later Pike's soldiers found him in a trading post. He had been ill, and his feet had been badly cut by the strings of his snowshoes. But the Lieutenant was happy.

"I found the headwaters of the Mississippi," he said. "I found some of the little lakes from which the great river flows. I have accomplished my mission, men.

"We will return to St. Louis in the spring—as soon as the river is free of ice. I'm anxious to send my reports and maps to President Thomas Jefferson."

Exploring the Great Plains

PRESIDENT JEFFERSON was deeply interested in Zebulon Pike's reports and maps. He presented them to the Congress at once.

"Now American settlers can go north into our new Purchase," he declared. "Now we know which tribes we can trust. We will be able to inform Americans moving there."

"We know now where to build forts to protect our settlers," said one congressman. "Lieutenant Pike's reports and maps are valuable. This officer had done a great service to his country."

The Lieutenant was sent on another expedition almost at once. He barely had time to visit his family. He had returned from the first expedition in the spring of 1806. In July he was setting out from St. Louis again.

In August he was promoted. It was Captain Zebulon Montgomery Pike who commanded this flatboat with its crew of nineteen men. There was also an interpreter.

"I have been instructed to explore the southern part of the Louisiana Purchase," Pike told him. "The United States must know exactly where the border is."

"That is wise, sir. Spain owns the land on the other side. It wouldn't do for American settlers to cross it by mistake. They might find themselves in some Spanish jail."

"No doubt, but neither the President nor Congress knows where this border is. Part of it is the Arkansas River, and part is the Red River. But no American seems to know just where these streams flow."

Captain Pike's expedition went up the Missouri River to the land of the Osage Indians—then up the Osage River to their largest village. This was the end of water travel. It was also the beginning of trouble and danger.

The interpreter found that Spanish troops had been to the Osage village a few days earlier. They had told the Indians that the United States would drive them from their homes and let them starve on the vast plains.

"What reason would the Spanish have for telling such things?" asked the Captain.

"Could it be that Spain wants this land? She owned it once, before she sold it to France."

"She may be getting ready to seize it. If she is, she will need these Indians to help."

The Osage chief pretended to make peace with President Jefferson's messenger. He took down the flag left by the Spanish troops. But he tried to prevent Pike from going on.

At first he refused to sell Pike horses for the land journey. The Captain was forced to offer a big price, but he finally got horses.

The explorers rode over the plains to the land of the Pawnee tribe. The Spanish troops had been here, too. They had given out many gifts— "along with their lies about Americans," said the Captain.

He finally persuaded the Pawnees to accept the American flag. But he allowed them to keep the Spanish flag in case the troops came back.

The Pawnee chief visited the Captain secretly. "I don't want trouble with the United States," he declared, "But my braves believe the lies the Spanish soldiers told. You must go back to your boats on the Osage River. If you try to go on, there will be bloodshed."

"I am not a woman to be frightened by threats," Captain Pike replied. "We will go on."

His words were bold, but his actions were

cautious. He led his men around the village when they started, and they thought they had escaped. But suddenly they were surrounded by Pawnee braves who demanded gifts.

The captain thought it wiser to yield, so he handed out presents.

"More! More!" the braves shouted, and they kept it up until there was nothing more to give. Then they began to seize the Americans' belongings. One brave tried to snatch the Captain's pistol from his belt.

Pike had tried to be patient. But now he drew his pistol and held it ready to shoot. "I'll kill the next brave who lays a hand on any one of us!" he shouted angrily.

Then the Americans were allowed to ride on toward the land of the Kansas tribe.

The Kansas tribe agreed to make peace with the United States, although the Spanish troops had visited them.

"The Kansas don't intend to keep peace with us," said Captain Pike. "But we did get some valuable information from them. Their chief told me how to find the Arkansas River. He said the Red River flows into it. All we have to do is to follow the Arkansas until we come to the Red."

This wasn't easy. In places the Arkansas was dry and the explorers lost it in the great sea of high grass. They lost days trying to find it again. Then, once they did locate it, they would track it under the burning sun.

The Americans pushed on and on through an endless sea of saddle-high, saw-tooth grass. Their clothing was torn and their legs were cut. Swarms of large flies stung the riders and their horses. One day the expedition was caught in a buffalo herd and had to ride through it.

"Have you noticed that we are climbing all the time?" Captain Pike asked his men one day. "The land is rising gradually. We should see mountains before long. Then I believe we'll find the source of the Red River. It will flow from some mountain lake, unless I'm mistaken."

The Captain was right about the mountains. One day his party saw a blue range in the distance. Soon Pike and his men began to suffer from the cold. Their lightweight clothing was no protection against the icy winds.

"I was misled about our clothing," explained the Captain. "The General thought we'd have summer weather all the time out here."

Now the game became scarce, and food supplies began to run low. Some of the men became ill from the lack of food and the bitter cold. All suffered from frozen hands and feet.

Huts were built for a winter camp. As usual, Captain Pike was the strongest man in the party. He nursed the sick. He went hunting and found game when others found none. He gathered wood to keep fires going.

"I'll have a report to make about this climate," he said. "General Wilkinson will be astonished."

"He should come here in November with only light clothing," the interpreter said.

"I must go on or I won't be able to get to the mountains before deep snows," said the Captain. "Then I'll find neither lake nor river."

He went on with three men. They thought the mountains were near, so they carried no food. They expected to find game on the way. But there was no game, and they walked three days before they reached the first mountain.

It was almost dark when they found a cave to sleep in. It was bitterly cold. They had to huddle together to keep warm.

That morning Captain Pike went out first to look about. Here was a sight so wonderful he was overcome. A great snow-covered mountain peak rose high above the range. It was a picture of beauty against the bright-blue sky.

Now the others joined him. They, too, were overcome by the sight.

"I have never imagined anything so beautiful as this peak," said one.

"It seems to be in eternal sleep," said another.

"In all this world there can be nothing more perfect," said the Captain. "I wish everyone might see its sublime beauty. It is like a glimpse of Heaven."

"It is worth the misery of the trip just to see it," said one.

"I would not miss it for ten times our troubles," said the Captain. "I wish we might climb it. But that is, of course, impossible in this zero weather and in our light clothing.

"We'll have to give up our search for the Red River until spring. Then we will bring the other men here. They must see this beautiful cone-shaped peak."

But things didn't happen that way. Before spring came Captain Pike and his men had been captured by the Spanish and taken into Mexico.

His captors said he was a spy and forbade him to make any maps or write any reports. But a "traveler" who had started from New Jersey when he was three years old, and who had been traveling ever since, was a good observer. He remembered a great deal of what he saw.

When Captain Pike was released in July, 1807, he relied on his excellent memory to prepare reports for President Thomas Jefferson. The President, in turn, presented these reports to the Congress of the United States.

"Gentlemen," said the President, "Captain Pike's expedition has been a success. Heretofore, the lower part of the Louisiana Purchase has been a complete mystery to us. Now, thanks to Captain Pike, we know many things about this area.

"A hundred times, this courageous explorer might have turned back, but he didn't. He steadfastly pushed on and on.

"Gentlemen, we owe Captain Zebulon Montgomery Pike our deepest gratitude and greatest admiration. Only time will tell just how valuable his expedition was."

190

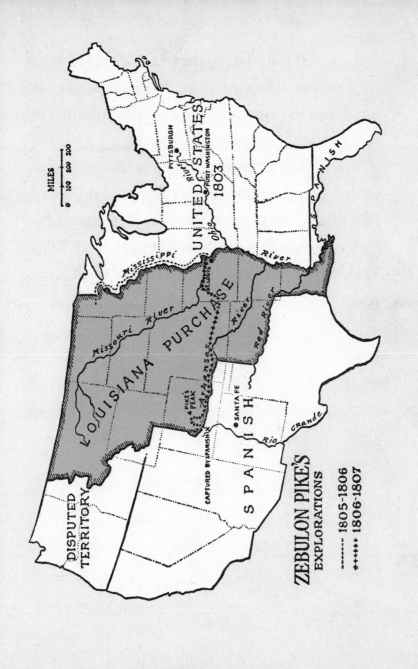

MILES
0 100 200 300

PITTSBURGH

Ohio River

FORT WASHINGTON

UNITED STATES
1803

S P A N I S H

Mississippi River

Missouri River

ST. LOUIS

Red River

LOUISIANA PURCHASE

ARKANSAS River

PIKE'S PEAK

CAPTURED BY SPANISH

SANTA FE

Rio Grande

S P A N I S H

DISPUTED
TERRITORY

ZEBULON PIKE'S
EXPLORATIONS

------- 1805-1806
+++++ 1806-1807

Time did tell. Today the Great Plains, crossed by Zebulon Pike's small party of explorers, are inhabited by American farmers who till the rich soil and reap a bountiful harvest.

Today thousands of Americans live at the foot of that grand mountain peak discovered by Captain Pike. The glory of this dazzling sight is forever a tribute to a great explorer. Indeed, Pike's Peak remains as a natural monument to a famous American.

More About This Book

WHEN ZEB PIKE LIVED

1779 ZEBULON MONTGOMERY PIKE WAS BORN NEAR LAMBERTON, NEW JERSEY, JANUARY 5.

The thirteen British colonies were fighting for independence from Great Britain.

The population of the thirteen colonies was over 2,000,000.

George III was King of Great Britain.

1779–
1783 ZEB LIVED IN NEW JERSEY WITH HIS MOTHER WHILE HIS FATHER FOUGHT IN THE REVOLUTIONARY WAR.

Cornwallis surrendered at Yorktown, 1781.

The peace treaty with Great Britain, ending the Revolutionary War, was signed, 1783.

1783–
1794 ZEB GREW UP IN FRONTIER SETTLEMENTS IN PENNSYLVANIA AND OHIO.

The Constitutional Convention met to frame the United States Constitution, 1787.

George Washington became the first President, 1789.

1794– ZEB PIKE SERVED IN THE UNITED STATES ARMY
1805 ON THE FRONTIER.

George Washington died, 1799.

The National capital was moved from New York to Washington, D.C., 1799.

Thomas Jefferson became President, 1801.

The United States bought the Louisiana Territory from France, 1803.

1805– PIKE EXPLORED NORTHERN AND SOUTHERN
1807 PORTIONS OF THE LOUISIANA TERRITORY.

Lewis and Clark explored the Northwest, 1804-1806.

Robert Fulton built the "Clermont," first practical steamboat, 1807.

1807– PIKE CONTINUED TO SERVE AS AN OFFICER IN
1813 THE UNITED STATES ARMY.

Abraham Lincoln was born, 1809.

John Jacob Astor organized the Pacific Fur Company, 1810.

Louisiana became a state, 1812.

The United States declared war against Great Britain, 1812.

194

The population of the country was about 7,900,000.

There were eighteen states in the Union.

James Madison was President.

DO YOU REMEMBER?

1. Where did the Pike family move when Zeb was eight years old?

2. How did Zeb manage to rescue his little brother Jimmie from the big wildcat?

3. What two boys became Zeb's neighbors and friends in the wilderness?

4. What happened to the covered wagon which a stranger brought into the community?

5. What kind of fight about George Washington did the boys have at school?

6. Why did Lester Mills tie Zeb in a cave?

7. How did Zeb kill his first bear?

8. What special work for the government was Captain Pike asked to undertake?

9. Why was Zeb allowed to accompany his father?

10. What secret passage did Zeb and Amos find at the trading post?

11. What did Captain Pike do with Mr. MacFeeters before leaving the trading post?

12. Where did the Pike family move when Zeb was fourteen years of age?

13. What fight did the settlers have with Indians while they floated down the river?

14. How did the soldiers and settlers repulse the Indians at Fort Washington?

15. How did Pike explore the upper Mississippi River for President Jefferson?

16. What great mountain peak did Pike discover on a later expedition for President Jefferson?

IT'S FUN TO LOOK UP THESE THINGS

1. What was the Louisiana Purchase and why did it mean much to our country?

2. What different Indian tribes did Pike come across in his trips to the West?

3. How did the Indians get the horses which they used in attacking settlers?

4. What explorations did Spaniards from Mexico make in the West?

5. Where is Pike's Peak and how high is it?

6. Why did early explorers travel on rivers wherever possible?

INTERESTING THINGS YOU CAN DO

1. Build a model of a frontier fort similar to a fort described in this book.

2. Collect pictures of Pike's Peak to display on the bulletin board.

3. Make a list of explorers besides Pike who helped to open up the West for settlement.

4. Draw an outline map of the United States and color the part that formerly was known as Louisiana Territory.

5. Read about the buffalos that once were found in the West and give a report to the class.

6. Find out how the Plains Indians lived differently from Indians in the East.

OTHER BOOKS YOU MAY ENJOY READING

Daniel Boone, James Daugherty. Viking.

Explorer's Digest, Leonard Clark. Houghton.

Louisiana Purchase, Robert Tallant. Trade Edition, Random House. School Edition, Hale.

Meriwether Lewis: Boy Explorer, Charlotta M. Bebenroth. Trade and School Editions, Bobbs-Merrill.

Pike of Pike's Peak, Nina Brown Baker. Harcourt.

Trails West and Men Who Made Them, Edith Dorian and W. N. Wilson. Whittlesey.

Real Book about Explorers, Irvin Block. Doubleday.

We Were There with Lewis and Clark, James Munves. Grosset.

INTERESTING WORDS IN THIS BOOK

ague (ā'gū) : malarial fever which causes a person to chill and shake

ammunition (ăm'ù nĭsh'ŭn) : bullets and other objects prepared for shooting

astonished (ăs tŏn'ĭshd) : surprised, amazed

bouquet (bōō kā') : bunch of flowers

198

burrows (bûr′ōz) : holes dug in ground by animals, such as rabbits and chipmunks

commotion (kŏ mō′shŭn) : disturbance

current (kûr′ĕnt) : flow or movement of water in a certain direction

dugouts: canoes made by hollowing out logs

expedition (ĕks′pē dĭsh′ŭn) : journey made for a certain purpose; also group of people making a journey for a certain purpose

garrison (găr′ĭ sŭn) : body of soldiers living and serving in a military post or fort

gristmill: mill for grinding grain

gunrunners: persons who sell guns and ammunition illegally

headwaters: source or beginning of a river

herbs (ûrbz) : small plants used for medicine or for flavoring

hostile (hŏs′tĭl) : unfriendly

indigo (ĭn′dĭ gō) : dark shade of blue with a reddish tint

infantry (ĭn′făn trĭ) : branch of the army in which the soldiers fight on foot

interpreter (ĭn tûr′prĕt ēr) : person who translates from one language to another

loopholes: small openings in a wall through which rifles or other weapons are fired

mission (mĭsh'ŭn) : task, errand, assignment

moccasin (mŏk'å sĭn) : soft slipper without heels made from the cured skins of animals

observer (ŏb zûr'vẽr) : person who watches and listens carefully to remember details

persuaded (pẽr swād'ĭd) : convinced

possums (pŏs'ŭmz) : small tree-dwelling animals that carry their young in a pouch

sand bar: ridge of sand built up by currents, as in a river

scowled (skould) : frowned, looked angrily

sentries (sĕn'trĭz) : soldiers or others placed on guard or watch

stockade (stŏk ād') : wall or fence surrounding a fort, post, or settlement

tomahawk (tŏm'å hôk) : hatchet used as a weapon by the Indians

translate (trăns lāt') : change words and ideas from one language to another

trundle (trŭn'd'l) **bed**: low bed that may be rolled under another bed

weasel (wē'z'l) : small blood-thirsty animal that kills other small animals, as birds and mice